# THE READER'S THEATRE OF
# CLASSIC PLAYS

## ADAPTED BY HENRY GILFOND

## TABLE OF CONTENTS

ISBN 0-89187-475-5
Curriculum Associates, Inc.
North Billerica, MA 01862

Reprinted by arrangement with Walker and Company

15  14  13  12  11  10  9

# LITTLE GIRLS WISER THAN MEN

**from the story by
Leo Tolstoy**

*Two young girls, dressed in their Easter clothes, get into a little quarrel. The mother of one gets into the argument, then the mother of the other. Pretty soon, the whole town becomes involved. We have all been witness to such incidents. Sometimes they have a tragic ending. Sometimes their endings are most comical. This is the story of such an incident which took place in old Russia, but which might very well have happened right here.*

| THE CAST | | |
|---|---|---|
| | *Announcer* | *Malasha's Mother* |
| | *Malasha* | *Akulina's Grandmother* |
| | *Akulina* | *First Man* |
| | *Ivan* | *Second Man* |
| | *Boris* | *Third Man* |
| | *Akulina's Mother* | *Fourth Man* |

**THE SET**    A street in a Russian Village of many years ago

**LITTLE GIRLS WISER THAN MEN is an adaptation by
Henry Gilfond of the short story of the same title by Leo Tolstoy.**

**This adaptation © 1966 by Henry Gilfond**

| Announcer | (Malasha and Akulina enter as the Announcer introduces the playlet.) This is old Russia. We are in a small village. It is Easter time. Easter has come early this year and the little streams and puddles left by the melting snow have not yet been completely dried up by the sun. Malasha and Akulina, two young Russian girls dressed up in their holiday clothes, are enjoying the season. |
|---|---|
| Malasha | This is the time of the year I like best. I think spring is the happiest season of the year. |
| Akulina | (Touching the earth) The earth becomes soft. |
| Malasha | The grass begins to grow. |
| Akulina | The birds begin to sing. |
| | (Malasha whistles like a bird. They both laugh.) |
| Malasha | And we get pretty new clothes. Do you really like my new dress, Akulina? Is it really pretty? |
| Akulina | It's really beautiful, Malasha. I love the way the skirt flares out. |
| Malasha | (Does a little dance, twirling to show off her new dress.) You really like it? |
| Akulina | I do. The prettiest dress I ever saw. |
| Malasha | Yours is prettier. |
| Akulina | How can you say that? Look how narrow my skirt is. |

| | |
|---|---|
| *Malasha* | But such a lovely blouse, with all those lovely colors. And the pleats in your skirt. I wish my skirt was pleated. |
| *Akulina* | Oh, Malasha! You know how much I wanted a flared skirt. *(She does a little dance.)* My skirt goes nowhere when I dance. |
| *Malasha* | Then you sing and I'll dance. *(She pauses.)* Akulina, do you know what? |
| *Akulina* | Let's change dresses? |
| *Malasha* | What would your mother say? |
| *Akulina* | Oh, please! She's already said enough. |
| *Malasha* | *(Imitating mother)* Be careful the way you wear that dress. |
| *Akulina* | *(Joining the game of imitating)* That dress cost a lot of money. It isn't one of your cheap skirts and blouses. |
| *Malasha* | *(Still imitating)* Watch where you walk. |
| *Akulina* | *(Still imitating)* Don't let it get torn. |
| *Malasha* | And keep it clean! *(They both laugh again.)* |
| *Malasha* | I think we've got the prettiest dresses in the village. |
| *Akulina* | *(Slyly)* I think we're the prettiest girls in the village. |
| *Malasha* | Akulina! |
| *Akulina* | That's what I think. |

| | |
|---|---|
| Malasha | Shush! *(She looks around.)* That's what I think, too. *(They begin to laugh again, and Ivan, a young boy, enters.)* |
| Ivan | *(Stops to look at the two girls who are still laughing.)* What's the joke? |
| Akulina | Ivan! |
| Malasha | We didn't recognize you. You're so dressed up. |
| Ivan | It's Easter, isn't it? |
| Malasha | Ivan, look! *(She does her little dance.)* |
| Ivan | Very pretty. And you look pretty too, Akulina. |
| Malasha | Hadn't you noticed before? |
| Ivan | Sure, I've noticed. But you look very nice in those new dresses. |
| Akulina | Thank you. You look handsome in your new suit, Ivan. |
| Boris | *(Entering)* What are you people talking about? You look so serious. Something happen? |
| Ivan | We're talking about the weather. What's it to you? |
| Boris | Nice weather. That's what it is to me. I'd like to play in that little stream running down the street before the sun dries it up. |
| Ivan | Grown-ups don't play in streams. |
| Boris | Oh yeah! How about the summertime? |
| Ivan | It's not summertime now. |

| | |
|---|---|
| Malasha | Well, I'm going to play in the stream. It's really a little lake. |
| Akulina | In your new dress? And your new shoes? |
| Malasha | I'll take my new shoes off. |
| Ivan | *(Taking his shoes off)* I'm taking mine off right now. |
| Malasha | How about you, Akulina? |
| Akulina | Let's. *(Beginning to remove her shoes)* But no splashing. I don't want any mud on this dress. |
| Malasha | *(Removing her shoes)* And I don't want any mud on mine. |
| Boris | You're all crazy. You're just going to get messed up. And then you'll catch it at home. |
| Ivan | Go home, Boris. Go home before you get drowned. |
| Boris | Not me. I'll just hang around and see the fun. |
| Malasha | *(Who has walked into the puddle of water)* It's deep, Akulina. *(Pretending)* I'm scared! |
| Akulina | *(Beginning to enter the puddle)* Nothing to be afraid of. It won't get any deeper than that. |
| Malasha | This is fun. |
| Ivan | The water is cold! |
| Akulina | Careful, Malasha. You're going to splash me! |
| Malasha | Don't worry. I'm being careful. *(And she splashes the water.)* |

**8**  *Little Girls Wiser Than Men*

| | |
|---|---|
| Akulina | *(Reacting sharply, the mud all over her face and dress.)* I told you to be careful! |
| Malasha | I was careful! |
| Akulina | *(Examines the mud on her clothes and grows more and more angry.)* You've ruined my dress! *(She moves quickly towards Malasha.)* I'll get you for this! |
| Malasha | *(Trying to get away)* It wasn't my fault! I didn't mean it! |
| Akulina | You've ruined it! |
| Malasha | I didn't mean it! Akulina! Please! |
| Akulina's Mother | *(Entering)* What is all this shouting about! *(She sees Akulina's dress.)* Oh! What have you done? Is this the way you treat your new clothes? Is this what I spend money for? |
| Akulina | Malasha did it, Mama! She's jealous of my new dress and she did it on purpose! |
| Malasha | I didn't! |
| Akulina | She did! She did! She did it on purpose! |
| Malasha | I didn't! I tell you, I didn't! |
| Akulina's Mother | You didn't, hey? *(She grabs Malasha and gives her a sharp smack.)* You didn't, hey? |
| Malasha | *(Crying loudly)* I didn't! I didn't! |
| Malasha's Mother | *(Entering)* What happened? Why are you crying? |

**10**  *Little Girls Wiser Than Men*

| | |
|---|---|
| *Malasha* | Akulina's mother hit me. |
| *Akulina's Mother* | Look what she did to my daughter's dress! |
| *Malasha's Mother* | Why did you hit my daughter? |
| *Akulina's Mother* | I said, look what your daughter did to my daughter's dress! |
| *Malasha's Mother* | And I asked you why did you hit my daughter! |
| *Akulina's Mother* | All the money I spent on that dress! |
| *Malasha's Mother* | I should whack you for whacking my daughter. |
| *Akulina's Mother* | Where am I going to get her another dress? |
| *Malasha's Mother* | If I gave you one good whack, maybe you wouldn't whack my daughter again. |
| *Akulina's Grandmother* | *(Entering)* Women! Women! This is Easter. This is no time for quarreling. |
| *Akulina's Mother* | This good-for-nothing child ruined Akulina's dress, and now her good-for-nothing mother threatens to strike me! Have you ever heard of such a thing? |
| *Malasha's Mother* | I'll soon show you who's a good-for-nothing mother! |

*(A crowd of neighbors, men, women and children have been gathering, and both Malasha and Akulina disappear from the scene.)*

| | |
|---|---|
| *First Man* | Go to it, woman! Show her who's a good-for-nothing! |
| *Second Man* | Why don't you leave them alone? |
| *First Man* | Why don't you mind your business? |
| *Second Man* | This is my business. This is a holy day. |
| *First Man* | You might remember that before you attack another gentleman. That is, if you are a gentleman. |
| *Second Man* | Are you accusing me of not being a gentleman? |
| *First Man* | Did I accuse you? Did I say you were a doctor? a thief? |
| *Third Man* | Gentlemen! Gentlemen! |
| *First Man* | He accused me of being a thief! |
| *Fourth Man* | A thief? Thief! Thief! There's a thief in the crowd! Watch your purses, ladies! |
| *Second Man* | I've a mind to let you have this good right fist in your mouth! |
| *Fourth Man* | Try it! |
| | *(As this fighting goes on, Malasha and Akulina return. Malasha has cleaned the mud off her dress and the dress is as good as new. Malasha has a ball. She tosses it to Akulina. Akulina returns the toss. They are the best of friends again.)* |
| *Third Man* | Gentlemen! Gentlemen! |
| *Malasha's Mother* | Let me get at her hair! |
| *Third Man* | Ladies! Ladies! Your children are wiser than you are. |

| | |
|---|---|
| Akulina's Mother | *(Who has not heard the Third Man)* My daughter's dress! Ruined! |
| Malasha's Mother | *(Who has not heard the Third Man either)* She slapped my daughter! She'll pay for it! |
| Third Man | Ladies! Ladies! Gentlemen! Look at the children! They are far wiser than their elders! |
| | *(There is a sudden hush. Everyone turns toward the two girls, who are playing ball.)* |
| Malasha | I still think that your dress is the prettiest dress I've ever seen. |
| Akulina | And I still think yours is the prettiest. |
| Malasha's Mother | What are we fighting about? |
| Akulina's Mother | I'm sure I don't know. |
| Malasha's Mother | You gave my daughter a good whack. She probably deserved it. |
| Akulina's Mother | No, no. I shouldn't have raised my hand to her. It is Akulina I should have whacked. |
| Malasha's Mother | Why? Children! That's all they are. Children! |
| Third Man | And much wiser than some ladies and gentlemen I see here. |
| All | *(As they exit)* Right. |
| Akulina | Do you like Boris? |

| | |
|---|---|
| *Malasha* | Maybe. |
| *Akulina* | I mean, do you really like him? |
| *Malasha* | Do you like Ivan? |
| *Akulina* | Do you like Boris? |
| *Malasha* | (*Smiles*) Today, I think, I like everybody. (*And she goes into her little dance, with her skirt flaring.*) |

# THE DUEL

## from the story by
## Alexandre Dumas

*As the title tells us, this a story of a challenge to a fight to death, a duel. But this is an unusual duel. Although the arms to be used are pistols, which is not unusual in a duel between soldiers, only one of the pistols would really be loaded—the other would carry a blank cartridge. The procedure was neither very common, nor very unusual. The pistols were to be held no more than six inches from the heart of each duelist. Even this was not unusual in such duels. What made this duel so strange? Oh, yes, someone will live and someone will die. But who? Will it be the young and handsome, hot-tempered Captain Zodomirsky, who is engaged to marry beautiful Mariana? Or will it be the cool, calm, and jealous Lieutenant Stamm?*

*There is a surprise in this story. As a matter of fact, there are several surprises. And the surprises are what make this duel so unusual.*

| THE CAST | Announcer | Lieutenant Stamm |
|---|---|---|
| | Major Belayef | Koloff (A servant) |
| | Captain Pravdine | Captain Stephen |
| | Lieutenant Michael | Mariana |
| | Lieutenant Naletoff | Doctor |
| | Captain George Zodomirsky | |

| THE SETS | Officers' room |
|---|---|
| | Captain Zodomirsky's apartment |
| | Dueling grounds |
| | Mariana's home |

THE DUEL is an adaptation by Henry Gilfond of the short story of the same title by Alexandre Dumas.

This adaptation © 1966 by Henry Gilfond

| | |
|---|---|
| *Announcer* | We are in the officers' room of a regiment of soldiers stationed in a small village in Austria. Among the officers are Major Belayef, Captain Pravdine, Captain Stephen, Lieutenant Michael, Lieutenant Naletoff, and Lieutenant Stamm. They are sitting around a table. They have just finished their breakfast, and the talk is lively. |
| *Stamm* | Tell me, anyone! What made the Colonel so excited this morning? |
| *Michael* | A new officer. We're getting a new officer, a new captain to join us. |
| *Naletoff* | Who is he? Do you know? |
| *Stephen* | What's his name? |
| *Pravdine* | Where does he come from? |
| *Michael* | One at a time. Gentlemen! |
| *Belayef* | All right! What's his name? |
| *Michael* | Zodomirsky! That's his name! Captain Zodomirsky! and he's engaged to that beautiful woman, Mariana! |
| *Belayef* | When does he get here? |
| *Michael* | He's here now. He should be here any moment. By the way, Captain Stephen, you must know him. You were both in the same regiment once. In St. Petersburg, I think. |
| *Stephen* | We studied together. I knew him. I knew him well. |
| *Belayef* | What kind of man is he? |
| *Stephen* | You'll like him. Everyone in St. Petersburg liked him. He has a temper, though, and it's a quick one, too. |

| | |
|---|---|
| *Stamm* | Mariana tells me that he is also quite a duelist. |
| *Stephen* | So he is! |
| *Stamm* | I don't like quick tempers, Stephen. If this Zodomirsky tries his temper on me, I'll cool it off. |
| *Naletoff* | A big order, Stamm, if the rumors are true! |
| *Stamm* | I've taken on big orders before. Reputations are made and reputations can be broken. |
| *Koloff* | *(Opens the door)* Gentlemen, Captain Zodomirsky! |
| *Michael* | *(As Zodomirsky enters)* Welcome! Welcome, Captain Zodomirsky! *(To the other officers)* Captain Zodomirsky! *(To Zodomirsky)* These are your new comrades. Brave soldiers and good fellows, every one of them! |
| *Zodomirsky* | I'm happy to join you, gentlemen! Proud to join you! *(To Stephen)* Ah, Captain! You haven't forgotten me, have you? |
| *Stephen* | Forget you? How could I? Welcome, Captain Zodomirsky! Glad to have you with us! |
| *Belayef* | How long are you going to be with us, Captain Zodomirsky? |
| *Zodomirsky* | For a long time, I hope! I've already got myself a quiet little house, a good cook, a small library, and a garden. It isn't St. Petersburg, but it's comfortable, and I've already set up a little target for practice shooting. |
| *Stamm* | Ah! You practice shooting? |
| *Zodomirsky* | Why, of course! |
| *Stamm* | You like shooting, don't you? |
| *Zodomirsky* | Yes! I like shooting! What about it? |

*The Duel* **17**

| | |
|---|---|
| *Stamm* | Shooting makes no sense to me, unless you're hunting. |
| *Zodomirsky* | You don't mean that, do you? |
| *Stamm* | It's exactly what I mean. Shooting makes no sense unless you are hunting. |
| *Zodomirsky* | I think you're mistaken, sir! A quick word sometimes leads to a quarrel, and a quarrel to the use of pistols. A man who is a good shot will shut the mouth of a fellow who amuses himself by asking useless questions. |
| *Stamm* | So that's why you practice! |
| *Zodomirsky* | A good enough reason, isn't it? |
| *Stamm* | I don't know. There should be some element of chance in a duel. A man of honor shouldn't practice his shooting *before* a duel. It gives him a dishonorable advantage. |
| *Zodomirsky* | Explain that, Lieutenant! |
| *Stamm* | Gladly. Do you play cards? |
| *Zodomirsky* | What's that got to do with it? |
| *Stamm* | I'll explain. I'll explain it so that everyone in the room can understand it. |
| *Zodomirsky* | Explain it, then! |
| *Stamm* | Well then, the man who is clever with cards can shuffle them so that he's always the winner. I can't see the difference between robbing a man of his money and robbing him of his life. |
| *Zodomirsky* | You've explained well enough, sir! Captain Stephen will see to it that this quarrel between us is ended *properly*! You won't refuse me, will you? |

| | |
|---|---|
| Stamm | As you wish, Captain. You said you practice shooting every day. I don't practice at all, except on the day of the duel. The odds would favor you, but I'll see to it that our chances are equal. I'll settle all the details with Captain Stephen. *(He exits.)* |
| Pravdine | *(To all the officers)* We can't let them fight, gentlemen. |
| Zodomirsky | Captain! Forgive me. I don't know why, but this man meant to insult me. There is no other way out. |
| Naletoff | He's jealous of you! Don't you know? He's in love with Mariana! |
| Zodomirsky | All the more reason, gentlemen, for the duel! Stephen! Please! You will make all arrangements, won't you? |
| Stephen | I don't like this, Zodomirsky! Is there no way of stopping this? What of Mariana? |
| Zodomirsky | Mariana will understand. |
| Stephen | But her heart is weak. Her doctors have said so. We, who have admired her from a distance, know it. You must know it, too. The shock might kill her! |
| Zodomirsky | She won't hear of the duel until it's over. Please, Stephen! |
| Stephen | She will hear of it. Stamm will be sure that she hears of it. No! She will hear of it some other way! |
| Zodomirsky | It is an affair of honor. Her honor, now, as well as mine. Wasn't it Stamm's jealousy that brought about the quarrel. It is Mariana's duel as well as mine. Make the arrangements, Stephen... |
| Announcer | Captain Stephen visited Lieutenant Stamm and it |

was all settled. Captain Stephen and Captain Pravdine are spending this last evening before the duel with Captain Zodomirsky, but Mariana, as Captain Zodomirsky was warned, has learned of the duel. As this scene begins, she has burst into Captain Zodomirsky's apartment.

| | |
|---|---|
| Mariana | (Breathlessly, to Zodomirsky) George! |
| Zodomirsky | Mariana! What are you doing here? |
| Mariana | You ask me why I'm here? I came to say good-bye! |
| Zodomirsky | Good-bye? But why, Mariana? Why? |
| Mariana | Why? Why? You keep asking why, and this may be the last time I will ever see you! |
| Zodomirsky | You're too excited, Mariana. You shouldn't have come! |
| Captain Stephen | (Making a move to leave Mariana and Zodomirsky alone) Excuse us, please. |
| Mariana | Stay! I beg you to stay! |
| Pravdine | We must go. Excuse us. |
| Mariana | Stay! As you are gentlemen, stay! I have nothing to hide. I want you to hear me. (To Zodomirsky) You must not fight this duel. |
| Zodomirsky | Mariana! |
| Mariana | I beg you. I command you! You must not fight this duel. Both of you will be killed! Your life belongs to me! Don't throw it away in this senseless duel! |
| Zodomirsky | What are you saying, Mariana! If I do not fight, I will be called, and rightly called, a coward! The shame would kill me more certainly than Stamm's bullet! |

| | |
|---|---|
| *Mariana* | *(To Pravdine)* Have pity on me, Captain! Tell him that he doesn't need to fight! Speak to him, Captain! If he won't listen to me, he'll listen to you! Speak to him! I beg you! |
| *Pravdine* | You know the arrangement for the duel? |
| *Mariana* | Yes! It is not a duel! It's an assassination! Please speak for me, Captain! |
| *Pravdine* | I would if I could. I cannot ask Zodomirsky to disgrace his uniform. It is a very unhappy moment for me, but Zodomirsky must fight, as Stamm has asked him to fight. There is no other way, except to dishonor the regiment. |
| *Zodomirsky* | You don't want me to disgrace my regiment, Mariana? You would be ashamed of me. How could you love a man who had lost his honor? |
| *Mariana* | It isn't that I would love you less, but that you would hate me for what you call dishonor. |
| *Zodomirsky* | Mariana! |
| *Mariana* | You are right. How could Stamm set such dreadful conditions for the duel! But you are right. *(Pause)* Perhaps we shall never see each other again. Good-bye, my love. Good-bye! *(She quickly moves out.)* |
| *Announcer* | The time for the duel has come. Zodomirsky and Stamm and their seconds are present. So are the other officers of the regiment. Stephen reviews the conditions. |
| *Stephen* | There are two swords on the ground. Zodomirsky, you will stand at this end of the swords. Stamm, you will stand at the other end. Each will hold one |

**22**  *The Duel*

|            | pistol. *(To Stamm)* You have put a bullet in one pistol and a blank cartridge in the other? |
|------------|---|
| Stamm      | That is correct. One pistol is harmless. The other pistol will kill. |
| Stephen    | And you yourself have loaded the pistols? You know which carries the real bullets? |
| Stamm      | That is correct, too. Captain Zodomirsky will choose the pistol he wishes to use. |
| Zodomirsky | Let's get on with it! |
| Stamm      | I am ready. |
| Stephen    | Take your positions! |
| Stamm      | *(Opening a case with two pistols, to Zodomirsky)* Choose! |
|            | *(Zodomirsky takes one without examining the guns at all.)* |
| Stephen    | Your positions, gentlemen. *(They take their positions.)* |
| Stamm      | *(Very quietly, as if to himself)* He is very brave. |
| Stephen    | When I count three, you will fire. *(Zodomirsky and Stamm point their guns at each other, no more than six inches from the heart.)* Ready, gentlemen? |
| Zodomirsky | Ready. |
| Stamm      | Ready. |
| Stephen    | One.....Two.....Three! |
|            | *(Zodomirsky shoots. He has shot a blank cartridge.)* |
| Zodomirsky | *(To Stamm, as the officers grow tense) (Calmly)* Shoot! |

**24** *The Duel*

| | |
|---|---|
| Stamm | It isn't your business to give me commands, Captain Zodomirsky. It's up to me, whether I shoot or not. And whether I shoot or not, depends on how you answer my question. |
| Zodomirsky | Your question, then! Ask it quickly! |
| Stamm | I'll ask it quickly enough. First let me say that I didn't come here to kill you. You are rich, Captain Zodomirsky. You are loved. You have a good future before you. I have none of these. But it is you who must die, and not I. |
| Zodomirsky | Your question! |
| Stamm | I've come to it. *(Pause)* Give me your word not to be so quick to fight duels and I will not fire. |
| Zodomirsky | *(Calmly)* You insulted me. I challenged you to a duel. I have nothing more to say. Fire! |
| Stamm | Your promise will not dishonor you. *(To the Major)* Major Belayef, you be the judge. Will Captain Zodomirsky dishonor himself if he accepts my conditions? |
| Balayef | Captain Zodomirsky has behaved with honor, and bravely. It will not be his fault, if he is not killed. *(To the other officers)* Is it honorable for Captain Zodomirsky to accept these conditions? |
| Officers | It is! It is! It is! |
| Pravdine | Captain Zodomirsky accepts your conditions. |
| Stamm | I haven't heard Captain Zodomirsky speak. |
| Pravdine | *(To Zodomirsky)* Say I have spoken for you, Zodomirsky! Please! Do you agree with what I have said? |

| | |
|---|---|
| Zodomirsky | *(Almost in a whisper)* I agree. |
| Officers | Hurrah! Hurrah! Hurrah! *(They embrace Zodomirsky with joy.)* |
| Stamm | I am happier than all of you. Everything has ended the way I wished it to end. *(To Zodomirsky)* I've shown you, Captain, that when the conditions are equal, a bad marksman is as good as the best marksman in a duel. I didn't want to kill you. I did want to see how you'd look at the face of death. You are a courageous man. My compliments. Neither pistol carried a live cartridge. *(He shoots his gun to prove it.)* |
| Zodomirsky | *(A cry of anger)* You are more insulting than you were before! Ended? Nothing is ended! We begin again. And this time, we load the pistols, if I have to do it myself! |
| Stamm | No, Captain. I gave you your life. I'm not taking it back. Insult me, if you want to. I'm not going to fight you. |
| Pravdine | Then you'll have to fight me, Stamm! |
| Naletoff | And if Pravdine doesn't kill you, I will! |
| Officers | I! I! I! |
| Stamm | I can't fight you all! Choose one, and I'll fight him! It won't be a duel! It will be an assasination! Choose! |
| Balayef | Calm, gentlemen! Calm! *(To Stamm)* You can't fight us all. Most likely you will fight none of us. You are to be judged! Gentlemen! You will be witness! *(To Stamm)* Sir, you have dishonored your uniform! You made Captain Zodomirsky go through all the feelings of a man condemned to die, while all the time you knew that neither gun was loaded, and felt perfectly safe. You refused to fight with Captain Zodomirsky, although you had insulted him twice. |

| | |
|---|---|
| Stamm | I'll fight him! I'll fight him! Where are the pistols? |
| Bayalef | No! No, sir! You will fight with none of us. You have dishonored your uniform You will hand in your resignation from the regiment. You will resign at once. |
| Stamm | I will resign. Not because you want me to, but because it is I who wish to resign *(He exits quickly.)* |
| Zodomirsky | Why did you make me agree to this ugly man's conditions? I should never have agreed. |
| Balayef | You acted with honor, Captain. You acted with courage. *(To the Officers)* Let us go, gentlemen. I have a report to make to the colonel. |
| Announcer | No one was killed by a pistol this morning, but the duel claims a victim. Zodomirsky hurries to the home of Mariana as quickly as he can, but Mariana, waiting at her window, has already seen another man in uniform. It is a doctor who greets Zodormirsky at Mariana's house. |
| Zodomirsky | Is it Mariana? |
| Doctor | Yes. |
| Zodomirsky | How ill is she? Tell me, Doctor! |
| Doctor | She is dead. |
| Zodomirsky | Dead. |
| Doctor | Dead. |
| Zodomirsky | Mariana! But she was alive and well just last night? How, Doctor? How? |
| Doctor | She saw Lieutenant Stamm ride back from the dueling grounds. She thought that meant you were dead. I had warned her. I had told her to avoid any strong emotion. But she saw Stamm ride by, and her heart gave way. |
| Zodomirsky | Mariana! Mariana! Mariana! |

# THE LADY OR THE TIGER?

## from the story by Frank R. Stockton

Behind one closed door is a ferocious, hungry tiger. Behind a second closed door is a beautiful young lady. In front of both doors stands a handsome young man, and he must choose which one to open. If he opens the one which will release the tiger, he will be clawed to death. If he opens the other, the beautiful young lady will become his wife. Why must this young man choose one of the doors? Which door will he open? Of course, he does not know which door hides the lady and which the tiger, but someone who is watching this ceremony—and it is a ceremony—does; and this person will show by a sign which door she wants the young man to open. Don't be sure that she will point to the door with the beautiful young woman behind it!

| THE CAST | Announcer | Second Guard |
|---|---|---|
| | The Princess | First Lady-in-waiting |
| | The Young Man | Second Lady-in-waiting |
| | First Guard | Messenger |

| THE SETS | Palace grounds |
|---|---|
| | The Princess's room in the palace |

THE LADY OR THE TIGER? is an adaptation by Henry Gilfond of the short story of the same title by Frank R. Stockton.

This adaptation © 1966 by Henry Gilfond

**29**

| | |
|---|---|
| Announcer | This story takes place in a time which is almost forgotten, in the small kingdom of a ruler with some rather savage ideas. Most savage, perhaps, was his idea of justice. When a man was accused of a serious crime — and it was the King who judged whether a crime was serious or not — he was sent into a huge arena like those in which Roman gladiators fought and early Christians were sent to battle with ferocious lions. Under this savage king, however, the accused had a little more choice. In the arena, he was put face to face with two closed doors. Behind one closed door was a beautiful young lady, behind the other, a man-eating tiger. The accused opened one of the doors. If the tiger emerged, the huge crowd which came to witness the "trial" saw the accused man cruelly clawed to death. If the young lady emerged, the accused man was married to her on the spot and was free to live with his young wife, happily ever after. |
| | As this story opens, we see a Young Man speaking with the Princess, the King's only daughter. For a young man who is not of royal blood — and this young man is not of royal blood — it is very, very dangerous to speak with a princess, especially if that princess becomes too much interested in him. |
| Princess | (A little angry with the Young Man) I didn't see you at the arena this morning. Where were you? |
| Young Man | I was there, Princess. I saw you, and you were more beautiful than ever. |
| Princess | (Losing her anger quickly) You did see me. That's why I looked so beautiful. I always look beautiful when you see me. |
| Young Man | More and more beautiful. |

*The Lady or the Tiger?*

| | |
|---|---|
| *Princess* | *(Saddening, just slightly)* The poor man. It was such a ferocious tiger. Why must the tiger always be so ferocious? |
| *Young Man* | It's what your father...the King...chooses. |
| *Princess* | I know. But the one this morning leaped so cruelly at the poor man. You noticed? |
| *Young Man* | No, Princess. I didn't notice. |
| *Princess* | You are as cruel as my father! |
| *Young Man* | No, my Princess. |
| *Princess* | You turned your face, then? You couldn't bear to see the man killed? You have a tender heart, my lover. |
| *Young Man* | No. No, my Princess. I am not afraid of killing, or of being killed. I'm a soldier, and I'm afraid my heart is not as tender as you might like it. But my eyes, my Princess, when they are near you, can look on nothing else. |
| *Princess* | *(Playing)* What do your eyes do when they're not near me? There are so many young and pretty girls in the court. Do you have eyes for them, too? |
| *Young Man* | *(Teasing)* Would you have me be blind to them? Of course I look at them. What else would you have me do? |
| *Princess* | *(Savagely)* I would have you be blind to them! I am the Princess! I order you to be blind to them! |
| *Young Man* | You command and I obey. |
| *Princess* | *(Softening)* Because I am the Princess, or because you love me? |
| *Young Man* | How shall I answer you, when you are so angry? |

| | |
|---|---|
| *Princess* | I'm not angry any more. Tell me. Why will you obey me? Because I am the Princess, or because you love me? |
| *Young Man* | *(Quietly)* I love you, Princess. |
| *Princess* | Because I am the Princess? |
| *Young Man* | No. |
| *Princess* | Oh, I do love you. I love you more than all these royal clothes I wear, more than the crown I must wear, more than the whole kingdom. *(Changing her tone)* Yet, I saw you talking with that young lady of the court. I see you talking with her often. |
| *Young Man* | *(Protesting)* She is just another lady of the court. |
| *Princess* | But she's very pretty, isn't she? |
| *Young Man* | I haven't noticed. |
| *Princess* | You haven't noticed her? Oh, not at all! She is the most beautiful lady in the whole court. How can I believe that? |
| *Young Man* | There is only one beautiful lady in this court, and it's my Princess. |
| *Princess* | That's why you speak to her so often! I've seen you speak with her for hours without end! |
| *Young Man* | Princess! What makes you so angry with me this evening? Suddenly, I am looking at all the women in the court. Suddenly, I've become involved with every woman in the kingdom. Something is troubling you. Something has happened. Tell me. |
| *Princess* | *(Very soft)* Nothing. Nothing, my love. I've been harsh. I've been unkind. But there is nothing to worry about. |
| *Young Man* | You are worried, Princess. |

| | |
|---|---|
| Princess | (After a pause) Yes. There is something. I should tell you. |
| Young Man | Tell me, Princess. |
| Princess | My father, the King, knows. |
| Young Man | Knows what, Princess? |
| Princess | He knows about us. He knows how much you love me. |
| Young Man | But the whole kingdom loves you. |
| Princess | Not the way you love me, my lover. Worse, he knows how much I love you. |
| Young Man | You spoke with him? |
| Princess | No. That would have been foolish, knowing how he feels about royal blood marrying royal blood. It was others. |
| Young Man | Are you certain? |
| Princess | I'm certain. Too many people have seen us together. |
| Young Man | I'm not sorry we were seen together. I'm not sorry that I love you so much. And how can I ever be sorry that you have loved me? |
| Princess | And love you still! But aren't you afraid of what will happen? |
| Young Man | What can happen? |
| Princess | The arena! The tiger! I can't bear to think of it! |
| Young Man | Don't think of it. We are together now. |
| Princess | And tomorrow it may be the arena! |
| Young Man | Tomorrow is far away, Princess. Besides, perhaps the King doesn't know about us. |

**36** *The Lady or the Tiger?*

| Princess | You are not frightened by the arena. You know that I will learn what is behind each door. You are sure I will give you a signal, so that you won't open the door to the tiger! Do you think I will let you marry another woman! *(Her tone has changed.)* Oh, how can I speak this way? How can I be angry with you? *(She sees two guards approaching.)* Oh, my lover! Here they come! What shall I do? |
|---|---|
| | *(The guards enter. They stop in front of the young man.)* |
| First Guard | You are under arrest! |
| Second Guard | In the name of the King, you are under arrest. Follow us! |
| | *(The Young Man looks once at the Princess, then follows the guards out. The Princess puts her hand on her mouth to stifle a cry.)* |
| Announcer | The Young Man has been arrested and imprisoned in a cell. It may seem to us today that to be in love is not a crime, royal blood or no royal blood. However, the King was the supreme ruler in those days, and in his kingdom it was a crime for an ordinary man to be in love with a princess of royal blood. The Young Man would be tried in the arena. He would have to choose a door, choosing the lady or the tiger. As the play continues, we see the Princess in her palace with two of her ladies-in-waiting. |
| Princess | Tomorrow he will be in the arena. The fault is mine as much as his. Why doesn't my father send me into the arena? |
| Second Lady | You are his daughter. |

| Princess | I know I am his daughter! But we should both have been accused, or neither of us! Where is my messenger? He has been gone too long! He is slow! There's no time! |
|---|---|
| Second Lady | Be patient, Princess. |
| Princess | I have no patience! I can't be patient! |
| First Lady | But you know which door hides the tiger. |
| Princess | Yes. It wasn't the easiest thing in the world to discover. They keep it a great secret. But I know which door is which! |
| First Lady | Then your young man will be saved, Princess. |
| Princess | Perhaps. Where, oh where is that messenger? *(The ladies-in-waiting are very quiet. The Princess looks at them, rather angrily.)* Because I know what is behind each door doesn't mean that he will know! How shall he know which door to open? |
| Second Lady | He will look to you for a signal. |
| Princess | How will he know that I know which door conceals the tiger? Has anyone known before? |
| Second Lady | He will know, Princess, that you have made it your business to know which door is which. |
| First Lady | He will be expecting the signal. |
| Second Lady | Will you give him the signal, Princess? |
| Princess | *(Quietly)* Yes. It won't be easy. |
| First Lady | It shouldn't be difficult. A simple movement of a hand, a finger, will be enough. He will look for it. |
| Second Lady | And the eyes of everyone else will be on him, not on you. No one else will notice the signal. |

| | |
|---|---|
| *Princess* | Ah, you are both stupid! I move my hand, I move a finger, I glance to the right or to the left, ever so slightly! Do you think that that is all there is to it? I love the man! |
| *Second Lady* | We know that, Princess. |
| *First Lady* | Of course, we know. You have only to move your finger ever so slightly, as you said, and he will be saved. |
| *Princess* | Saved for what? Have you thought of that, you small-minded women? Where is the messenger? I love him, I told you! Do you think it will be easy for me to see him marry another woman? |
| *Second Lady* | But he will live. He will not be killed. |
| *Princess* | For you! He won't be killed for you! Messenger! Messenger! And I must choose, not he! I must choose whether the tiger will kill him, or whether he will marry the lady behind that other door. *(As the Messenger enters)* Ah! You're here at last. Ladies, please. I wish to be alone with this messenger. *(As the Ladies move aside)* What news do you have for me, messenger? Be quick! |
| | *(The Messenger whispers to the Princess.)* |
| *Princess* | Ah! *(Pause)* I will pay you well for this information. Later. You may go now. Go! |
| | *(The Messenger exits and the Ladies rejoin the Princess.)* |
| *Princess* | Why do you look at me? |
| *First Lady* | You have news, Princess? Bad news? |
| *Princess* | I have news. *(Pause)* I know the lady. The one behind the door, the one he will marry if he opens |

*The Lady or the Tiger?* **39**

it. Oh, she will not be unhappy to marry him. I've seen her look at him. And he has looked at her. They have spoken together often. I have seen them. She is beautiful, I must admit that. Too beautiful! Do not stare at me!

First Lady    We don't mean to stare, Princess. Excuse us.

Princess    You think I shall point to the door for the tiger! You think I am jealous! Think it, if you wish! It is my finger that will open the door. Which door? *(To herself)* Can I see him clawed, horribly clawed, and killed by the tiger? I love him. Can I see him marry this other woman? Can I? I love him. And tomorrow, tomorrow, I shall point to a door.

Announcer    On the morning of the following day, with the arena jammed with people, the Young Man looked at the Princess, and the Princess pointed. Without hesitation he moved to the door she had indicated and opened it.

Was it the tiger that emerged? Or was it the lady? The Princess was faced with a terrible problem. How did she solve it? The author of this story thought it was too deep a question to answer himself. How did the Princess decide? What answer did she find for the problem? How would any person decide? How would you decide? The Young Man opened a door. Which came out of that door, the lady or the tiger?

# DAVID SWAN

## from the story by
## Nathaniel Hawthorne

*Who is the young man who drops his knapsack on the side of a road and goes to sleep? A young girl will look at him and think him the most handsome young man she ever saw. A preacher will look at him and think him a drunkard. Two thieves will stop to rob him, kill him, if need be. Who is David Swan? What happens while he sleeps?*

| THE CAST | | |
|---|---|---|
| | *Announcer* | *Another Man* |
| | *David Swan* | *Gentleman* |
| | *Man* | *Lady* |
| | *First Woman* | *First Girl* |
| | *Second Woman* | *Second Girl* |
| | *Third Woman* | *First Thief* |
| | *Fourth Woman* | *Second Thief* |
| | *Fifth Woman* | *Driver* |
| | *Preacher* | *Passersby* |

THE SET     A road near Boston in about 1800

DAVID SWAN is an adaptation by Henry Gilfond
of the short story of the same title by Nathaniel Hawthorne.

This adaptation © 1966 by Henry Gilfond

| | |
|---|---|
| Announcer | *(As David Swan enters with his knapsack and acts out the speech of the Announcer)* This story takes place at a time when our country was very young. David Swan, a handsome young man, has been walking the unpaved highways. It is summer time. David Swan is tired. He stops for a moment, looks around. Another man enters. |
| David Swan | Good morning, sir. |
| Man | *(Looks up to the sky)* More like late afternoon, young man. |
| David | *(Laughing)* I should know that. Good afternoon, sir. I've been walking since the sun rose. |
| Man | You've walked a long distance. |
| David | I've still a distance to go. Is there a coach that takes this road? |
| Man | *(Suspiciously)* There is a coach that goes to Boston. Are you going to Boston? |
| David | Not by foot, any more. When does the coach pass by here? |
| Man | Before sundown. |
| David | *(Looks up at the sky again)* Then there is time to sit and rest my legs for a while. Thank you, sir. |
| Man | *(Still suspicious)* You carry a heavy sack. |
| David | All my goods. *(Putting it down, just off the road)* It will make a fine pillow. |

| | |
|---|---|
| Man | The road is not always safe. |
| David | It has never done me harm. |
| Man | There are highwaymen. |
| David | It is only a short time before sundown. The coach should be here soon. |
| Man | If it hasn't met with some accident...or some highwaymen. |
| David | In that case, I shall rest a little longer. Good day, sir. |
| Man | Good day. *(He exits.)* |
| David | *(Making a bed for himself, off the road, his knapsack his pillow)* A suspicious man. He suspects everybody. He suspects me, too. *(He chuckles, then falls asleep.)* |
| Announcer | David slept, and as he slept, a number of people walked near him. Some didn't notice him at all. Some remarked on the sleeping young man, and walked on. Some paused to study the sleeping figure before they, too, went on. |
| | *(A number of people walk across the stage, as the Announcer speaks.)* |
| First Woman | *(Looking at David)* Humph! |
| Second Woman | *(Laughing)* He is certainly sound asleep. |
| Third Woman | A lazy good-for-nothing! |

| | |
|---|---|
| Fourth Woman | *(Taking a longer look)* They come from every-where, these tramps! There should be a law against them! |
| Fifth Woman | How charming he looks in his sleep. |
| Preacher | A drunkard! And not ashamed! *(Picking up a stick)* I'll wake him and drive him out of here! |
| Another Man | Let him sleep, Preacher. He is doing you no harm. |
| Preacher | He harms himself. And if he harms himself, he harms all men. I'll wake him. |
| Another Man | Come, Preacher. Let him sleep it off. |
| Preacher | Or let him die there! |
| | *(They move off. A Lady and Gentleman enter, and stop in front of David.)* |
| Gentleman | How soundly he sleeps. |
| Lady | And so quietly. |
| Gentleman | He must be a healthy young man to sleep so soundly. He has no cares, no worries on his mind. |
| Lady | No. Only peace. The young sleep soundly. |
| Gentleman | I'd give half my land to have such peace, such sleep. |
| Lady | Do you think he was sent to us? |
| Gentleman | By whom? |
| Lady | He looks so much like Henry. |

**46** *David Swan*

| | |
|---|---|
| Gentleman | Henry is dead. |
| Lady | Perhaps heaven has sent this young man in our son's place. Shall I wake him? |
| Gentleman | Why? What do we know about this boy? |
| Lady | His sweet face. His sweet sleep. |
| Gentleman | Come! The sun will soon be down. |
| Lady | Let's wake him. |
| Gentleman | Come. I feel chilly. |
| | *(They move away, the Lady taking a last long look at the sleeping David. David does not stir. Two young girls enter. They are busy talking about their dreams. They do not notice David, as they stop in front of him.)* |
| First Girl | Mine will be tall, and dark, and very handsome. |
| Second Girl | Mine will be fair, and come from the sea. |
| First Girl | A sailor? |
| Second Girl | A captain. A hero of some big naval battle. |
| First Girl | Mine will be a soldier... Or a doctor... Or a minister... |
| Second Girl | Or an Indian chief. |
| | *(They laugh)* |
| First Girl | As long as he's not a thief. |
| Second Girl | *(Sees David, who is still asleep)* Thief! Look! *(They look.)* |

| | |
|---|---|
| *First Girl* | Do you think... |
| *Second Girl* | No. He's not a thief. |
| *First Girl* | He is so handsome. |
| *Second Girl* | I have never seen anyone so handsome. |
| *First Girl* | He would look better in better clothes. |
| *Second Girl* | To me, he is more beautiful than anyone I have ever seen. |
| *First Girl* | You're being silly. Who is he, anyway? |
| *Second Girl* | I don't care who he is. I'm going to wake him. |
| *First Girl* | *(Beginning to pull Second Girl away)* No, you're not going to wake him. Are you looking for trouble? |
| *Second Girl* | Please! |
| *First Girl* | Let's go! You must be going mad! |
| *Second Girl* | Perhaps. Perhaps. *(The Girls slowly exit, while David sleeps on.)* |
| | *(Two Thieves enter.)* |
| *First Thief* | Do you see what I see? |
| *Second Thief* | And no one else around. |
| *First Thief* | That's a big bundle he's got under his head. |
| *Second Thief* | I'll bet you a bottle of brandy that he's got a little gold tucked away in that bundle. |
| *First Thief* | If it's not in the bundle, it's in his trousers. |

| | |
|---|---|
| Second Thief | Suppose he wakes up? |
| First Thief | (Pulling out a knife) I'll be ready for him. |
| Second Thief | Then what are we waiting for? |
| First Thief | (Suddenly) Hush! |
| Second Thief | I can't hear anything. |
| First Thief | Of course you can't. There's nothing to hear. Shush! |
| Second Thief | Ready? |
| First Thief | You get the bundle. |
| Second Thief | (Begins to get the bundle, but changes his mind) You get the bundle. |
| First Thief | I've got the knife. I'll hold it close to him, in case he wakes up. You get the bundle. |
| Second Thief | If I move the bundle, he'll wake up. |
| First Thief | I've got the knife at his throat, haven't I? |
| Second Thief | You won't miss, will you? |
| First Thief | Here! You hold the knife, if you're afraid. |
| Second Thief | You can hold the knife. I'll get the bundle. |
| First Thief | Go ahead! Be quick! Before anybody walks in on us! (Second Thief moves to the bundle, then stops again.) What's the matter now? |
| Second Thief | I heard a noise. (There is the sound of twigs breaking.) |

| First Thief | Somebody in the woods. |
| Second Thief | Let's get out of here! *(Sound of a dog barking)* |
| First Thief | It's only a dog. |
| Second Thief | If it's a dog, it has a master with it. |
| First Thief | Maybe you're right. |
| Second Thief | You know I'm right! |

*(They exit. David sleeps on. Suddenly there is the sound of the stagecoach, the rumble of wheels on the road, the clatter of horses. David wakes up.)*

| David | *(Waking)* It was a good sleep. I had a good dream. What was it? I had several good dreams. And a bad one, too. *(Shouting out)* Hallo! Hallo there, Stagecoach! Hallo there, driver! *(The stagecoach comes to a stop.)* Which way, driver? |
| Driver | *(Entering, with his whip)* *(He stretches his legs.)* Glad you called me. It's been a long ride. My legs needed stretching. Which way are you going? |
| David | I'm going to Boston. Which way are you going? |
| Driver | Boston. What takes you there? Work? |
| David | Yes, for my uncle. |
| Driver | On a ship? You look as though you might make a good sailor. |
| David | No. Groceries. I'm going to work behind the counter in my uncle's grocery store. |

| | |
|---|---|
| *Driver* | Well, that's an honest living for an honest young man. Hop aboard. You'll have to ride the top. That's all the room we've got left in this coach. |
| *David* | The top is good enough for me. |
| *Driver* | The best seat is on the top, really. |
| *David* | Sure. You can see more of the world that way. |
| *Driver* | More of its people, too. Hop on it now! We'll get to Boston before the whole town is asleep and dreaming. |

# THE NECKLACE

## from the story by
## Guy de Maupassant

*A woman is invited
to a very special kind of
party. She wants to look her
best, and so she borrows a necklace
from a good friend. She is the prettiest
woman at the party, and she has the best
time of her life. But she will have to pay for that necklace,
and she does. What kind of necklace was it? Why did she
have to pay for it? How did she pay for it? Guy de Maupassant
liked to give a special twist to the endings of his stories. What will
it be this time?*

THE CAST     *Announcer*
                   *Monsieur Loisel*
                   *Madame Mathilde Loisel (His wife)*
                   *Madame Jeanne Forestier*

THE SETS     The Loisel living room
                   The house of Madame Forestier
                   A boulevard in Paris

THE NECKLACE is an adaptation by Henry Gilfond
of the short story of the same title by Guy de Maupassant.
This adaptation © 1966 by Henry Gilfond

| | |
|---|---|
| Announcer | We are in the living room of Monsieur Loisel and his wife, Mathilde. It is the simple living room of a man who works hard and just manages to get along. He works as a clerk in the Ministry of Education, in Paris, France. Generally, he comes home tired, and he and his wife sit down to a simple supper. However, tonight is no ordinary night for Monsieur Loisel. He is obviously excited about something. |
| MonsieurLoisel | *(Entering and shouting)* Mathilde! Mathilde! |
| Mathilde | Here I am. Why are you shouting? |
| Loisel | Ah, Mathilde! My good wife! |
| Mathilde | You have been drinking, my good husband! |
| Loisel | Ah, no! Mathilde, let me tell you slowly. |
| Mathilde | *(Beginning to set the dinner table)* Very well. Tell me while we're having our supper. You got a raise? |
| Loisel | Ah! You are joking. |
| Mathilde | We need a new sofa, some curtains. It isn't a raise? |
| Loisel | No. Nothing so ordinary. |
| Mathilde | Then what? |
| Loisel | *(Pulling an envelope from his pocket)* For you! |
| Mathilde | An inheritance. My rich aunt has died and left me some money. |
| Loisel | No! No! Open the envelope! What a surprise! |
| Mathilde | *(Opening the letter)* You won some money in a lottery. *(She pulls an invitation card out of the envelope and looks at her husband, blankly.)* This is your surprise? |

| | |
|---|---|
| *Loisel* | Read it! |
| *Mathilde* | *(Reading)* The Minister of Education and Madame Ramponneau request the pleasure of the company of Monsieur and Madame Loisel at the Ministry on the evening of Monday, January 18th. |
| *Loisel* | We've been invited by the Minister of Education! What an honor, Mathilde! |
| *Mathilde* | *(Putting the invitation down and returning to the dinner table)* *(Sourly)* A great honor. Sit down and eat. |
| *Loisel* | But Mathilde! We have never been invited before. I thought...At least, I thought you'd be pleased. |
| *Mathilde* | Your soup is getting cold. |
| *Loisel* | Only a few clerks were invited. It took so much effort to get this invitation, Mathilde. Only the very best people will be there. |
| *Mathilde* | And what am I going to wear at such an important affair? |
| *Loisel* | *(For a moment he is stumped.)* The dress you wear when you go to the theater. Your theater dress. It's very pretty. |
| | *(Mathilde begins to cry.)* |
| *Loisel* | It's a beautiful dress, Mathilde. |
| *Mathilde* | A rag. A wretched dress. Like everything else in this house. This wretched table. These wretched chairs. The silver. This food. Is this the way to live? |
| *Loisel* | I do the best I can. |

| | |
|---|---|
| *Mathilde* | I know you do the best you can. It's not good enough. I was born to fine things, elegant furniture, thick rugs, shining silver. I have nothing. I am not going to your party! |
| *Loisel* | But Mathilde! |
| *Mathilde* | I'm not going. Give your invitation to one of your friends. Give it to someone whose wife has a decent dress to wear. |
| *Loisel* | *(Quietly)* How much would it cost to get a new dress? Something you can wear to the theatre. Or to an affair, when we are invited. How much would such a dress cost? |
| *Mathilde* | *(Thinks for a moment.)* I don't know exactly. |
| *Loisel* | About how much? I have some money saved. I had been thinking of buying a hunting gun for my vacation next summer. About how much, Mathilde? |
| *Mathilde* | *(After a pause)* I could buy a simple dress for four hundred francs. |
| *Loisel* | That's exactly how much I have saved. Four hundred francs. |
| *Mathilde* | Buy your gun, then. We don't need to go to the party. |
| *Loisel* | No. You buy a dress with it. Four hundred francs! You should be able to get a very nice dress for four hundred francs. |
| *Announcer* | Ah, Madame Mathilde Loisel was a happy woman! For once in her life she was able to go out and buy a beautiful dress in which to attend an elegant affair. There would be music, dancing, handsome young men, and an elegant table of elegant food, |

all beautifully served. Then, just a few days before the day of the party, Mathilde began to grow sad again. Monsieur Loisel was quick to notice.

**Loisel**    What's the matter with you? Don't you feel well?

**Mathilde**    I'm not sick, if that's what you mean.

**Loisel**    You should be laughing and singing! You're going to the most elegant affair in Paris. You've bought yourself a beautiful dress. Instead, you act as if you are the most unhappy woman in the world.

**Mathilde**    I am. I'm miserable. I'm absolutely miserable.

**Loisel**    Why?

**Mathilde**    You are absolutely blind. You can't see anything.

**Loisel**    I can't see what?

**Mathilde**    I haven't a jewel to wear. A necklace. A bracelet. A single stone. I'll look like no one at the party. Who'll notice me? Who'll look at me? Not a single jewel! *(And she begins to cry again.)*

**Loisel**    I'll buy you some flowers.

**Mathilde**    Flowers?

**Loisel**    For a few francs I can buy you some beautiful roses.

**Mathilde**    Flowers! Roses! Are we going to some picnic? You don't understand at all. You'll never understand.

**Loisel**    I try, Mathilde. I try to understand.

**Mathilde**    All the women there will be wearing diamonds. Diamonds! And I'll be wearing flowers!

**Loisel**    And what can I do about it?

**58** *The Necklace*

| | |
|---|---|
| Mathilde | Nothing! But I'm not going to the party. I'm not going to let myself look foolish, with all those rich women and their diamonds! |
| Loisel | Then we won't go to the party! |
| Mathilde | I should have known that from the very beginning. You bring me an invitation. You might as well have lost it. This is no kind of party for people as poor as we are. |
| Loisel | *(With a sudden bright idea)* How about Madame Forestier? She is a good friend of yours. She's rich. She has more diamonds than she can wear. She'll lend you a bracelet, a necklace, something, for one evening. |
| Mathilde | *(Suddenly quite happy)* Of course! Why didn't I think of it? Of course she'll lend me a bracelet, a necklace... |
| Announcer | Very early the next morning, Madame Loisel called on her friend Madame Forestier, and Madame Forestier was most generous. |
| Madame Forestier | Of course, my dear. I'll be happy to let you have anything you'd like. *(Producing a box of jewels)* Here. Choose what you like. |
| Mathilde | Oh! How beautiful! You are so kind. *(She looks at the jewels.)* Is there anything else you have? |
| Madame Forestier | *(Producing another box)* Perhaps there is something here you fancy. |
| Mathilde | Beautiful! Beautiful! Have you anything else, Madame Forestier? If it isn't too much trouble... |
| Madame Forestier | No trouble at all. *(She produces several boxes.)* |

| | |
|---|---|
| Mathilde | Ah! *(She looks at everything. Finally, she picks up a beautiful diamond necklace.)* This! *(Putting the necklace around her throat)* May I borrow this beautiful necklace? |
| Madame Forestier | It's lovely on you. You may borrow anything you like. |
| Mathilde | Oh, thank you! Thank you! I'll return it in the morning! |
| Announcer | Madame Loisel was the happiest woman in Paris. And at the elegant party, she was gayer and happier than she had ever been before, in all her life. All the handsome young men had their eyes on her, and they all danced with her. But parties must end, and early the next morning, Monsieur and Madame Loisel arrived at home weary, but quite happy. |
| Mathilde | What a glorious evening. |
| Loisel | I'm glad you enjoyed it. *(Moving to help Mathilde take off her cloak)* Let me help you. |
| Mathilde | No. Let me remember for a little while. |
| Loisel | It's late, Mathilde. I have to get up early. I work tomorrow. |
| Mathilde | *(Allowing Loisel to help her with her cloak)* Of course. Of course. But it was a beautiful evening! *(She reaches towards her throat for the necklace.)* It isn't there! *(Her mood changes quickly.)* |
| Loisel | What is it, Mathilde? |
| Mathilde | The necklace! It's gone! |
| Loisel | It can't be. Look in your dress! In your bag! |
| Mathilde | *(As they both search frantically)* It's not here! I've lost it! |

**60** *The Necklace*

| | |
|---|---|
| *Loisel* | At the party? |
| *Mathilde* | No. I remember touching it, as we left. Did you take the number of our taxi? |
| *Loisel* | No. Did you? |
| *Mathilde* | No. What shall we do? A diamond necklace. It must be worth millions! |
| *Loisel* | I'll go back. I'll go over every inch of the way home. I'll find it. I must! |
| *Announcer* | But Loisel did not find it. The police couldn't find it. They advertised in the papers, offered a reward. The diamond necklace was not returned and they had to replace it. They found one like it for thirty-six thousand francs. |
| *Mathilde* | Even this may not be good enough. Even if we buy it, I hope Madame Forestier doesn't open the box it comes in. |
| *Loisel* | But where are we going to get thirty-six thousand francs? I couldn't save that much money in ten years. |
| *Mathilde* | Borrow it. I'll help pay it back. |
| *Loisel* | How? With what? |
| *Mathilde* | I'll work. I must return that necklace. |
| *Loisel* | But what kind of work can *you* do? |
| *Mathilde* | I can sew. I can help in someone's kitchen. I can clean. |
| *Announcer* | And that is exactly what Madame Loisel did, for ten years. They moved from their neat and comfortable house to a one-room apartment under a roof. There was no more theatre, and never a party. Mathilde scrubbed and scrubbed ... If it wasn't dirty dishes it was |

**62**  *The Necklace*

clothes. Both Loisel and his wife aged terribly in those years. They had borrowed money from everyone to buy that necklace for Madame Forestier. Ten years after she had borrowed the necklace Mathilde happened to meet Madame Forestier, whom she had not seen in all those years. The meeting took place on a great boulevard of Paris. Madame Forestier was ten years older but still elegant, still beautiful. Mathilde had become old and very plain.

| | |
|---|---|
| *Mathilde* | Good morning, Jeanne. |
| *Madame Forestier* | *(Looks at her. Obviously, she does not remember, or recognize, Mathilde.)* I don't know you, Madame. |
| *Mathilde* | I am Mathilde. Mathilde Loisel. |
| *Madame Forestier* | Oh! Mathilde! How you have changed! |
| *Mathilde* | I've had some hard times. And you, Jeanne, were the cause of my hardship. |
| *Madame Forestier* | I the cause? How is that? |
| *Mathilde* | Do you remember the diamond necklace you lent me? |
| *Madame Forestier* | *(Trying to remember)* The diamond necklace? |
| *Mathilde* | It was for the affair at the Ministry. Ten years ago. |
| *Madame Forestier* | Ah, yes. I remember. Well, it is a rather pretty necklace. |
| *Mathilde* | Beautiful! And I lost it. |
| *Madame Forestier* | Lost it? But you returned it to me. |

| | |
|---|---|
| *Mathilde* | No. I lost it. I bought another that looked like it. That's the one I returned. And we've been paying for it for ten years. It wasn't easy. You understand that. We are poor. But the debt is paid off now, and I'm glad. |
| *Madame Forestier* | *(Puzzled)* You bought a diamond necklace to replace mine? |
| *Mathilde* | You didn't notice the difference? I'm glad for that, too. |
| *Madame Forestier* | But, my poor Mathilde! |
| *Mathilde* | It's all over now. Thirty-six thousand francs, and we paid it all. |
| *Madame Forestier* | But, Mathilde! The necklace I lent you was not a diamond necklace. The stones were imitation diamonds. Surely, the whole necklace wasn't worth more than a few hundred francs! |

# THE CASK OF AMONTILLADO

## from the story by
## Edgar Allan Poe

*Edgar Allan Poe was a master of the short story. He was also a master of suspense. No other writer before or after has surpassed him in his ability to create fear, a sense of approaching disaster, sheer horror.*

*"The Cask of Amontillado" is a story of revenge. Montresor has hated Fortunato for a long time. He has plotted his revenge with great care. It is a horrible revenge. Will it work? We will not know the nature of the revenge until the story is almost at its end.*

THE CAST       *Announcer*
                    *Montresor*
                    *Friend*
                    *Fortunato*

THE SETS      A street in a town of Italy
                    Vault (wine cellar)

THE CASK OF AMONTILLADO is an adaptation by
Henry Gilfond of the short story of the same title by Edgar Allan Poe.
This adaptation © 1966 by Henry Gilfond

| | |
|---|---|
| *Announcer* | Let us go back to a time when men walked about the streets with swords at their sides, when tempers were quick, and when an argument was often settled by a duel — even to death. |
| | We are on a narrow, winding street in one of the many small towns in southern Italy. It is early in the morning. The sun has yet to appear over the horizon, and most of the people of the town are still asleep in their beds. The only men in the streets are those who have come from a carnival celebration. Montresor and a friend enter. Montresor is in high spirits, but he is completely sober. He is excited about some plan he is developing, but he speaks calmly and with deliberation. His friend is not quite so sober, but he recognizes the excitement in Montresor and he is troubled by it. |
| *Friend* | You are much too sober for me, Montresor. You hardly drank at all at the carnival. |
| *Montresor* | And you're a little too drunk, my friend. |
| *Friend* | I had my share, but I'm not drunk. Come. What are you waiting for? I'll see you to your door. |
| *Montresor* | I'll stay and rest here a while. Go, my friend. It's late. You've emptied too many bottles of the good wine. |

| | |
|---|---|
| Friend | (Suspiciously) You are meeting someone here, Montresor? |
| Montresor | Good night, friend! Or good morning! We'll meet again! |
| Friend | You are waiting for Fortunato. |
| Montresor | (Looks at his friend sharply, then softens) Why should I wait for Fortunato? |
| Friend | Your eyes were on him all night. |
| Montresor | My friend, you don't hold your wine as well as you used to. Why don't we say good night? |
| Friend | I will say good night to you at your door! You are too sober! Men are most dangerous when they are most sober. Come, Montresor! You'll meet Fortunato some other time. |
| Montresor | You worry too much. Tell me, my friend, are you worried about me, or are you worried about Fortunato? |
| Friend | I worry about you. I detest Fortunato as much as you do. |
| Montresor | But not with as much reason. He has offended me a thousand times. |

| | |
|---|---|
| *Friend* | And he will offend you **again tonight**. And you will draw your sword. There will be bloodshed. And you will pay for it. |
| *Montresor* | *(Laughs)* You are my friend, and you think I could be so crude, so foolish? |
| *Friend* | I would understand it. For years you have been nursing a hatred for Fortunato! You have planned your revenge. I'm sure! Is this the night he pays for all his insults? Tell me, Montresor! |
| *Montresor* | I tell you that it is late, and that you should have been home in your bed hours ago. |
| *Friend* | If you are my friend, Montresor, you will answer. |
| *Montresor* | Shall I give you my sword? If you take my sword and keep it in your house till this evening, will you feel the better for it? |
| *Friend* | *(Puzzled)* You have some more devilish scheme, then. What are you plotting, Montressor? |
| *Montresor* | You are too suspicious, my friend. Take my sword, or go home without it. It is getting late and whoever it is I am going to meet, I want to meet him alone. |
| *Friend* | I'll take your sword! God help Fortunato! *(He pauses)* And God help you, Montresor! Good night! |

| | |
|---|---|
| Montresor | *(As friend exits)* Good night, my friend. *(Montresor looks up and down the street.)* He should be here soon. *(He paces the street.)* I have waited a long time. How sweet this revenge will be. How delicate! How cruel! How well I've planned it. Where are you, Fortunato? You drank too much at the carnival. Your mind is fuzzy. Your legs are weak. It's your mind I must have this night, Fortunato! You walk this way every evening. This is the way to your house. *(He suddenly stops. He looks. A big smile comes over his face)* Fortunato! |

*(Fortunato enters. As we already know, he has had too much wine at the carnival. He doesn't stumble in his walk, but he is a bit unsteady. Although his mind may be a little fuzzy, he speaks clearly enough.)*

| | |
|---|---|
| Montresor | Fortunato! Well met! |
| Fortunato | Montresor. Are you the new night watchman? |
| Montresor | *(Laughs)* You joke again. *(As Fortunato begins to move on)* Don't leave me so quickly, Fortunato. *(He grasps Fortunato's arm, to stop him.)* I've been looking for you all over town. |
| Fortunato | *(Looks at Montresor's grip on his arm. Montresor releases his grip.)* I should think you would rather avoid me. |

| | |
|---|---|
| *Montresor* | *(Laughing)* You are jesting again! |
| *Fortunato* | With you, Montresor? Or at you? |
| *Montresor* | Ah, you are in good form, Fortunato. And how well you look today. You've never looked better. |
| *Fortunato* | *(Pleased, even if it is Montresor who is complimenting him)* Why shouldn't I look better? The wine at the carnival was good. *(Suspiciously)* What is on your mind, Montresor? You said you've been looking for me. |
| *Montresor* | Yes, I've been looking for you. Nobody else would do. |
| *Fortunato* | Do for what? |
| *Montresor* | You do like a good wine, Fortunato, don't you? |
| *Fortunato* | *(Suspiciously)* You have a good wine? |
| *Montresor* | I'm not sure. That's the point. No one in the whole country knows wines better than you do. |
| *Fortunato* | I won't disagree with you. |
| *Montresor* | No one would disagree. That's why I've been looking for you. I've just received a cask of Amontillado. At least, I was told it was Amontillado. |
| *Fortunato* | At this season of the year? Amontillado? |

| | |
|---|---|
| *Montresor* | I have my doubts, but I had to buy it on the spot. I looked for you before I bought it. |
| *Fortunato* | Not Amontillado! |
| *Montresor* | I couldn't find you anywhere, so I took the chance. |
| *Fortunato* | It can't be Amontillado. |
| *Montresor* | Maybe you're right. There's only one way to make sure. Will you test it for me? Of course, if you're too busy, I could ask my friend, Luchesi. He knows wines, too. |
| *Fortunato* | Luchesi doesn't know the difference between sherry and cognac! |
| *Montresor* | Yet there are some fools who say Luchesi's taste for wine is as good as yours. |
| *Fortunato* | They're fools, indeed! Come, let's go to your wine cellar! |
| *Montresor* | Oh, no. I couldn't think of it. |
| *Fortunato* | Why not? |
| *Montresor* | You know my wine cellar. It's in the vault — the vault in which all the ancient Montresors are buried. |

| | |
|---|---|
| *Fortunato* | Vaults are the best place for wines. I didn't know you were so clever, Montresor. A vault keeps wines well. |
| *Montresor* | I can't ask you to come. You have a cold. The vault will chill you. I'll ask Luchesi. |
| *Fortunato* | The cold is nothing! Come! Did you say it was Amontillado? You've been fooled. It can't be Amontillado. As for Luchesi, he wouldn't know the difference. Let's go! |
| *Announcer* | Montresor and Fortunato enter the cold, damp vault in which the ancient Montresors have been buried. |
| *Fortunato* | The cask of what you call Amontillado? Where is it? *(Coughs)* |
| *Montresor* | Further on. How long have you had that cough? |
| *Fortunato* | *(Coughs)* It's nothing. |
| *Montresor* | Your health is more precious than the wine. Let's go back. You are a rich man, Fortunato. You are respected, admired. Loved. This damp air will kill you, and you are a man to be missed. *(Fortunato wants to answer but can only cough)* It's different with me. It doesn't matter whether I live or die. I can't let myself be responsible for your being ill, and getting worse. Luchesi will do for this Amontillado. |

| Fortunato | Nonsense! The cold is nothing. I won't die of a cough. |
|---|---|
| Montresor | True! True! *(Opening a bottle of wine)* Here, some of this Médoc will help us fight the damp air. Drink it. |
| Fortunato | *(Taking the bottle)* I drink to the buried who rest around us. *(He drinks.)* |
| Montresor | *(Drinking)* And I drink to your long life. |
| Fortunato | *(As they move on)* These vaults are rather large. |
| Montresor | We were a large family. The nitre in the vaults keeps the bodies. It also keeps the wine. |
| Fortunato | What was your family motto? I've forgotten it. |
| Montresor | "No one hurts me and gets away with it". Do you remember our coat of arms? A gold foot, crushing a serpent. |
| Fortunato | Very good! |
| Montresor | We are below the river bed now. Notice how thick the nitre is. Notice how the moisture trickles on the exposed bones of the skeletons. |
| | *(Fortunato coughs.)* |
| Montresor | You're coughing. Let's go back. |
| Fortunato | No, no! Let's have some more of that Médoc. |

**74** *The Cask of Amontillado*

| | |
|---|---|
| Montresor | *(Handing Fortunato a bottle)* Try some of this. |
| Fortunato | *(Drinks the whole bottle down, and drops the empty bottle with an odd twist of his wrist. He laughs, or rather giggles, a little bit drunk.)* You didn't understand that gesture? |
| Montresor | No. |
| Fortunato | Then you're not a member of the secret organization? You're not a Mason? |
| Montresor | Ah, but I am a mason. |
| Fortunato | You can't be. |
| Montresor | But I am. I am a mason. |
| Fortunato | A joke. Let's go on. |
| Announcer | They have moved to the end of the vault. Here there is a little room, four feet deep, three feet wide, six feet tall, just large enough for a man to stand up in. Someone was once buried there. |
| Montresor | The Amontillado is in that room. Go ahead. *(As Fortunato hesitates)* Now, Luchesi... |
| Fortunato | *(Moving into the room)* Luchesi is a fool! |
| Announcer | *(As Montresor acts out the announcer's words)* Montresor was fast. From nowhere, he got a rope and quickly tied Fortunato to the wall. |
| Fortunato | *(Still a bit drunk)* The Amontillado! |

**76**  *The Cask of Amontillado*

| Announcer | Montresor had the building stone and the mortar ready. He was really a mason then. He began to build a wall, a wall to seal up Fortunato in that small room. |
|---|---|
| Fortunato | What are you doing? What are you doing? |
| Announcer | And the wall was quickly finished. Montresor had buried Fortunato alive! |
| Fortunato | *(From behind the wall)* Good joke, Montresor! It's a good joke. *(He laughs.)* We'll laugh about it over a glass of wine. |
| Montresor | The Amontillado! |
| Fortunato | *(Laughing)* Yes, yes! The Amontillado! But let's go now. |
| Montresor | Where? |
| Fortunato | It's late. My wife will be waiting. Let's go now. |
| Montresor | Yes. Let's go! |
| Fortunato | For the love of God, Montresor! |
| Montresor | For the love of God! Yes! For the love of God! *(After a pause)* Fortunato. *(Another pause)* Fortunato! *(Another pause)* Fortunato!!! *(After a long pause)* Rest in peace, Fortunato. Rest in peace. |

# THE OPEN WINDOW

## from the story by
## Saki (H.H. Munro)

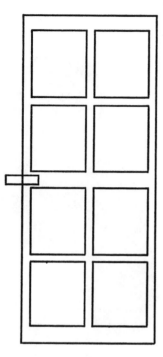

*Can three men who have
disappeared into the woods for
three years come back to life
again? This is a strange story,
with a stranger ending.*

**THE CAST**      *Mr. Sappleton*
*Mrs. Sappleton*
*Ronnie* (Mrs. Sappleton's young brother)
*Donald* (Another of Mrs. Sappleton's brothers)
*Vera* (Mrs. Sappleton's niece, about fifteen
years old)
*Mr. Nuttel* (A very nervous young man)

**THE SET**       The living room of the Sappleton country house,
its large French window wide open.

Illustrations adapted from the works of: Macke,
page 4; Bruegel (attribution now questioned), page 8;
Matisse, page 10; Macke, page 14.

THE OPEN WINDOW is an adaptation by Henry
Gilfond of the short story of the same title by Saki (H.H. Munro).

This adaptation © 1965 by Henry Gilfond

*Vera*

*Mr. Nuttel*

*Vera*

*Mr. Nuttel*

*Vera*

*Mr. Nuttel*

*Vera*

*Mr. Nuttel*

*Vera*

*Mr. Nuttel*

*Vera*

*Mr. Nuttel*

*Vera*

*Mr. Nuttel*

*Vera*

*Mr. Nuttel*

*Vera*

*Mr. Nuttel*

*Vera*

*Mr. Nuttel*

*Vera*

*Mr. Nuttel*

Won't you please come in.

(Nervous, entering) Thank you.

My aunt will be right down.

I'll wait.

Won't you sit down?

(Sitting, nervously) Thank you.

(Dropping into another chair) Meanwhile, you'll have to try to put up with me.

(Nervously looking around, but politely) I think I'll enjoy that.

Thank you. Do you know many people around here?

I don't know a soul.

(To be sure) Nobody?

My sister was here. About four years ago.

Oh?

Yes. She asked me to call on your aunt.

That was nice of her.

I hope your aunt thinks so.

Oh, she will. But you've never met my aunt?

No, I've never met her.

You know nothing about her?

(Nervously) Should I?

You've never heard about the tragedy?

Tragedy?

*Vera*

*Mr. Nuttel*

*Vera*


*Mr. Nuttel*

*Vera*

*Mr. Nuttel*

*Vera*

*Mr. Nuttel*

*Vera*


*Mr. Nuttel*

*Vera*

*Mr. Nuttel*

*Vera*

*Mr. Nuttel*

*Vera*

*Mr. Nuttel*

*Vera*


*Mr. Nuttel*

*Vera*

*Mr. Nuttel*

My aunt's tragedy.

(Nervously) No. I never heard of her tragedy. I'm sorry.

(Very quietly) It happened just three years ago. That must have been just after your sister left us.

Yes. Yes. I'm very sorry to hear it. Perhaps I ought to go.

No, no, no! Please stay.

(Not sure at all) Tragedy, you said?

Very sad. Very sad.

(Most uncomfortable) Sorry. Sorry.

Have you wondered why we keep the window wide open on an October afternoon?

It's quite warm. It's quite warm for this time of the year.

But the window's always open.

Oh? (Uneasily questioning) The tragedy?

The tragedy.

I see. I see.

You can't. Not unless you know.

And I don't know. No, I don't know. Of course.

It was on an October morning that they went out through that window.

(Looks nervously at the window) They?

My uncle. That's Auntie's husband. And her two brothers.

(Nervously) Three of them?

Vera

Mr. Nuttel

Vera

Mr. Nuttel

Vera

Mr. Nuttel

Vera

Mr. Nuttel

Vera

Mr. Nuttel

Vera

Mr. Nuttel

Vera

Mr. Nuttel

Vera

Mr. Nuttel

Vera

Mr. Nuttel

Vera

Mr. Nuttel

*(Nodding)* They walked right through that open window. With their guns. And their dog.

Hunting, I suppose?

Hunting.

Oh! October is the time of year for hunting.

It was exactly three years ago today. They walked through that window. *(Pause)* They never came back!

Oh?

They never came back.

Oh! They never came back?

No. *(Dramatically)* They got swallowed up in a swamp.

How dreadful!

It was terribly wet that year, you know. Places that were perfectly safe before suddenly gave way without warning.

Dreadful!

They never found the bodies.

Your poor aunt.

Yes, poor Auntie. That was the most awful part of it. They never found the bodies.

*(With much feeling)* I'm deeply sorry.

There's more.

You don't say!

There is.

Oh?

*Vera*

*Mr. Nuttel*
*Vera*

*Mr. Nuttel*
*Vera*

*Mr. Nuttel*
*Vera*

*Mrs. Sappleton*

*Mr. Nuttel*
*Vera*
*Mr. Nuttel*
*Mrs. Sappleton*
*Mr. Nuttel*

Poor Auntie. She always thinks they'll come back. "They'll come back some day," she says. Her husband, her two brothers and their little brown dog.

Oh, my!

She thinks they'll come back and walk back into the house through that window again, the way they used to when they were alive. That's why the window is kept open. All year around.

Poor woman.

Yes. Poor Auntie. She has told me so often how they went out, her husband with a white raincoat over his arm, and her brother Ronnie singing. He always sang, just to tease poor Auntie.

What a pity!

Yes, and do you know *(almost in a whisper)* sometimes, when it is very, very quiet here, I almost get a creepy feeling that they will come back, that the three of them, my uncle and the two brothers, and the dog, *will* come back. Right through that window.

*(Entering suddenly)* I'm sorry to have kept you waiting. So good of your sister to send you here. I hope Vera has been amusing you.

*(Carefully)* Vera has been very interesting.

Thank you.

Thank you.

I hope you don't mind the open window.

*(Quickly)* No, no! Not at all!

Mrs. Sappleton

Mr. Nuttel

Mrs. Sappleton

Mr. Nuttel

Mrs. Sappleton

Mr. Nuttel

Mrs. Sappleton

Mr. Nuttel

Mrs. Sappleton

Mr. Nuttel

Mrs. Sappleton

Mrs. Sappleton

Vera

My husband and my two brothers will be home very soon. They've been hunting and they always come into the house through that open window.

*(Anxiously)* So Vera told me.

Of course. They've been out in the marshes and they'll make a fine mess of my poor carpets. Just like all men, aren't they? But what brings you to this part of the country?

*(Nervous)* Nothing at all. Nothing at all, really.

No?

Oh, I've been ill and the doctors think I need a rest, a complete rest. That's what they've ordered. I'm not to do any work, or think too much. I'm to keep away from any kind of excitement.

Really?

*(Very nervous)* No excitement at all.

*(Looking out of the window, suddenly shouting)* Here they are!

*(Losing control)* Who?

My husband! My two brothers! And just in time for tea! Look how muddy those men are! I do hope they keep that dog out of here!


*(Mr. Nuttel, utterly panicked, runs out of the room.)*


I say! Mr. Nuttel!

He's gone.

Mrs. Sappleton

Mr. Sappleton

Mrs. Sappleton


Vera

Mr. Sappleton

Vera

Mr. Sappleton

Vera

Mrs. Sappleton

Vera


Mrs. Sappleton

Vera

Mrs. Sappleton

Vera

Mrs. Sappleton

(As Mr. Sappleton and the two brothers enter) A strange young man. (To Ronnie, who is singing) Now stop that foolish noise, or I'll send you to your room.

(The white raincoat on his arm) Who was that young fellow who just flew out of here? Looked like he was trying to catch a train.

A very strange young man, indeed. A Mr. Nuttel. You might remember his sister. She was here about four years ago. All he talked about was his illness. Then he ran off without so much as a good-bye. You'd think he had seen a ghost.

(Quietly) I think it was the dog.

The little brown dog? That dog wouldn't hurt a mouse!

Mr. Nuttel's terribly afraid of dogs.

Oh?

That's what he told me.

Strange young man. Tea?

He was hunted into a cemetery once, he told me — by a pack of wild dogs. He had to spend the whole night in an open grave, with all the dogs snarling at him. That's enough to make anyone afraid of dogs.

Now, Vera!

That's what he told me, Auntie!

That's one story of yours that I find very hard to believe, Vera.

But, Auntie!

But, Vera!

# THE ROMANCE
# OF A
# BUSY BROKER

**from the
story by
O. Henry**

This is a short play about three people and love. It has a surprise ending. The three people are Harvey Maxwell, Pitcher and Miss Leslie. Mr. Maxwell is a broker, and the boss. Pitcher is his right-hand man. Miss Leslie is their young and pretty secretary. The three people work in one small office. Love works in that office, too. It is a very small office, and very busy, but love can get into the smallest places and win its way into the hearts of the busiest people. . .

THE CAST      *Announcer*
                *Harvey Maxwell* (The very, very busy broker)
                *Pitcher* (His young right-hand man)
                *Miss Leslie* (The pretty secretary)
                *A Young Lady*

THE SET      A small office, three chairs, three desks, typewriter, filing cabinet, telephones, wall-clock

THE ROMANCE OF A BUSY BROKER is an adaptation
by Henry Gilfond of the short story of the same title
by O. Henry (William Sydney Porter).

This adaptation © 1966 by Henry Gilfond

**93**

| | |
|---|---|
| *Announcer* | This is the office of Harvey Maxwell. It is nine-thirty in the morning and Pitcher has been here since nine. He is busy at his desk, opening mail, reading letters. He looks at the wall-clock. He looks at his own watch. He opens another package of letters. *(Pitcher's actions follow the words of the Announcer.)* |
| | *(The telephone rings. Pitcher picks up the receiver.)* |
| *Pitcher* | Harvey Maxwell Company, Mr. Pitcher speaking. Good morning. Mr. Maxwell isn't here just now. He should be here at any moment. Is there anything... *(A click of the phone at the other end. Pitcher looks at the phone for a moment, then hangs up the receiver. The telephone begins to ring again.)* Harvey Maxwell Company, Mr. Pitcher speaking. Good morning. Is there anything I can do for you? Thank you. Good-bye. *(He holds the phone a moment, then hangs up the receiver. He looks at the clock, then goes back to the mail on his desk. The phone rings again.)* |
| | Harvey Maxwell Company, Mr. Pitcher speaking. Good morning. *(Another phone begins to ring.)* Just one moment, please. *(Into the first phone)* Sorry to have kept you waiting. *(Into second phone)* Sorry to have kept...*(He hangs up both phones, shrugs his shoulders, glances at the clock, and then returns to the letters on his desk.)* |
| | *(Harvey Maxwell and Miss Leslie open the door of the office and enter.)* |
| *Maxwell* | *(Brusquely, in a hurry)* Good morning, Pitcher. |

| | |
|---|---|
| *Pitcher* | Good morning, Mr. Maxwell. |
| *Maxwell* | *(Goes to his desk, sits down and begins to go through his mail)* Everything here, Pitcher? |
| *Pitcher* | Everything that came in this morning, except for these few letters on my desk. |
| *Maxwell* | You're slow this morning, Pitcher. |
| *Pitcher* | Here they are, Mr. Maxwell. *(Handing Mr. Maxwell the rest of the mail)* It is all sorted. Orders, cancellations, requests, inquiries... |
| *Maxwell* | I don't hear the phone. Is it out of order? Check with the telephone company! |
| *Pitcher* | There were several calls this morning. |
| *Maxwell* | Call the telephone company. Who called? What did they say? What did they want? |
| *Pitcher* | Personal calls, sir. |
| *Maxwell* | Personal? Nothing personal in this office, Pitcher! Who called? You're not very fast this morning, Pitcher, and this office calls for speed. We're a busy office, Pitcher. Who called? |
| *Pitcher* | They didn't say. They said they'd call again. |
| *Maxwell* | They didn't say? Wasting my time. *(The phone rings)* Answer it, Pitcher. This is a busy office, Pitcher. Answer the phone. |
| *Pitcher* | *(Already on the phone)* Harvey Maxwell Company, Mr. Pitcher speaking. Good morning. Who is calling, please? Just a moment, please. *(To Maxwell)* Mr. Stone of Stone and Company calling Mr. Maxwell. |

**96**   *The Romance of a Busy Broker*

| | |
|---|---|
| Maxwell | *(Picking up the phone)* Why didn't you say so? No, not you, Mr. Stone. Good morning. |
| Miss Leslie | *(As Maxwell speaks into the phone)* Good morning, Mr. Pitcher. |
| Pitcher | Good morning. |
| | *(They smile at each other, then Miss Leslie walks slowly to Maxwell's desk, and smiles at him as he talks into the phone. Maxwell scarcely notices her.)* |
| Maxwell | *(Still at the phone)* Of course, Mr. Stone. Agreed, Mr. Stone. We're very busy here, Mr. Stone. Goodbye. *(He hangs up the phone and looks at Miss Leslie, who is still smiling at him.)* Well? |
| Miss Leslie | Nothing. |
| Maxwell | I'm busy! I'm very busy! *(To Pitcher)* Pitcher! The stock sheets! The market reports! The Wall Street columns! |
| Pitcher | *(Making the deliveries)* Yes, sir. |
| Miss Leslie | *(To Pitcher)* You called yesterday? |
| Pitcher | Called? |
| Miss Leslie | About getting a new girl, a new secretary. |
| Pitcher | Of course. |
| Miss Leslie | Someone has to take my place here. It is a busy office. *(She is smiling again.)* |
| Pitcher | I know. I know. *(The phone rings)* Harvey Maxwell Company, Mr. Pitcher speaking. Good morning. Who is calling? Just a moment, please. *(To Maxwell)* Mr. Green of Green and Smith. |

| | |
|---|---|
| Maxwell | (Picking up phone) Mr. Smith! |
| Miss Leslie | Did you call, Mr. Pitcher? |
| Pitcher | Call? Oh, yes! I made several calls. |
| Miss Leslie | No luck? |
| Pitcher | They haven't sent anyone yet. |
| Miss Leslie | Oh, well. I might as well sit down and get to work. That is, until the agency sends somebody. The work's got to be done. |
| Pitcher | That's very good of you. |
| Miss Leslie | (Sitting down) Thank you, Mr. Pitcher. |
| | (There is a knock at the door.) |
| Pitcher | Come in. The door is open. |
| | (A young lady enters.) |
| Young Lady | Is this Mr. Maxwell's office? |
| Pitcher | Yes. Mr. Maxwell's very busy, miss. Can I help you? |
| Young Lady | The agency sent me. |
| Miss Leslie | Can you type? And take shorthand? |
| Young Lady | I was tops in my class. |
| Pitcher | (After looking her over) Just a minute, miss. (To Maxwell) Mr. Maxwell... |
| Maxwell | (His eyes glued to his desk) Yes? |
| Pitcher | There's a young lady to see you, sir. |
| Maxwell | What does she want? Take care of her. I'm busy. |

| | |
|---|---|
| *Miss Leslie* | She's from the agency. |
| *Maxwell* | What agency? Take care of her, Pitcher. There are too many interruptions in this office. Can't you see what she wants? *(To Young Lady)* I'm sorry, miss, but you can see how busy I am. Pitcher! |
| *Pitcher* | She's here to see you about the job, Mr. Maxwell. |
| *Maxwell* | What job? There are no jobs to be had in this office. We could use the help, I suppose, but I'm much too busy to get it. |
| *Pitcher* | The secretary's job, Mr. Maxwell... |
| *Maxwell* | We have a secretary, Pitcher. Do I need to remind you? We have a secretary. |
| *Pitcher* | But you asked me to call, Mr. Maxwell, and I did. I called the agency and they've sent this young lady. |
| *Maxwell* | You must be mad, Pitcher. Miss Leslie is the best secretary we ever had. Why should I want anyone else? *(To the Young Lady)* There's been a mistake. Tell your agency there's been a mistake. I'm sorry, miss. And I'm very busy. Busy! Busy! |
| *Young Lady* | *(Shrugs her shoulders)* Everybody makes a mistake sometime. *(To Pitcher)* He certainly is a busy man. *(She exits.)* |
| *Maxwell* | *(To Miss Leslie)* You must excuse Pitcher. He must be working too hard. Your place is secure here, Miss Leslie. You've been doing a very good job. You can stay here as long as you want to. The job is yours, Miss Leslie. It's yours for as long as |

**100** *The Romance of a Busy Broker*

|            |                                                                                                                      |
|-----------:|----------------------------------------------------------------------------------------------------------------------|
|            | you want it. *(To Pitcher)* Do you hear that, Pitcher?                                                                |
| Pitcher    | I was only doing what you asked, Mr. Maxwell.                                                                         |
| Maxwell    | Forget it. You had better call that agency. Tell them not to send me any more girls. We don't need them, do we, Miss Leslie? |
| Miss Leslie | Thank you, Mr. Maxwell.                                                                                              |
| Maxwell    | Well, Pitcher? Why aren't you calling? I don't want a parade of young women in here. I'm much too busy.               |
| Pitcher    | *(At the phone)* But I am, sir.                                                                                       |
| Maxwell    | Good. *(To Miss Leslie)* Miss Leslie, please take a letter.                                                           |
| Miss Leslie | *(Sitting down with her pad and pencil)* Of course, Mr. Maxwell.                                                     |
| Maxwell    | *(His head up in the air)* Mr. John Smith…440 Main Street…*(He stops, looks at Miss Leslie, very closely.)*           |
| Miss Leslie | *(Repeating)* Mr. John Smith…440 Main Street…                                                                        |
| Maxwell    | You look very pretty today, Miss Leslie.                                                                              |
| Miss Leslie | *(Sweetly)* Thank you.                                                                                               |
| Maxwell    | *(Dictating the letter again)* Dear Sir…*(He can't go on.)*                                                           |
| Miss Leslie | Dear Sir…                                                                                                            |
| Maxwell    | *(Gets up from his chair, walks up and down the office floor, stops in front of Miss Leslie.)* *(Very quickly)* Miss Leslie! |

| | |
|---|---|
| *Miss Leslie* | Yes? |
| *Maxwell* | I've just got one minute. |
| Miss Leslie | Yes? |
| *Maxwell* | You know how busy I am. I'm always busy. |
| *Miss Leslie* | I know you're a very busy man, Mr. Maxwell. |
| *Maxwell* | Well, I've got a minute now. It's a very short minute, Miss Leslie, but I must ask you a very important question in this short minute. You understand, Miss Leslie, that I'm a most very busy man. I want your answer to that very important question, Miss Leslie. |
| *Miss Leslie* | In a minute? |
| *Maxwell* | Less than a minute now, Miss Leslie. |
| *Miss Leslie* | I'll try, Mr. Maxwell. |
| *Maxwell* | I wish you would, Miss Leslie. |
| *Miss Leslie* | The question, Mr. Maxwell? |
| *Maxwell* | Ah, yes, the question. I've just a minute, Miss Leslie. Will you be my wife? |
| *Miss Leslie* | *(Shocked, speechless for a moment)* What did you say? |
| *Maxwell* | I said, will you be my wife? I know that this isn't the normal procedure for courting a young lady, for wooing her, but you know how busy I am. I just haven't the time to buy flowers and chocolates, and so on. Forgive me, Miss Leslie. But tell me, will you be my wife? Talk quickly, please! |

|  | I've a million letters to read, a million letters to get out into the mail. |
|---|---|
| Miss Leslie | *(Still in shock)* Just what are you talking about, Mr. Maxwell? |
|  | *(ALL THE PHONES IN THE OFFICE BEGIN TO RING. PITCHER IS GOING MAD TRYING TO ANSWER ALL OF THEM AT THE SAME TIME.)* |
| Maxwell | Don't you understand? I want to marry you. I want you to marry me. I love you, Miss Leslie. I've wanted to tell you that for the longest time, but all these phones, all these letters. *(To Pitcher)* Answer the phone, Pitcher! Can't you see I'm busy? Tell them to wait! *(To Miss Leslie)* Will you marry me? You must tell me now. At once. You see how busy I am. I can't wait another minute. Will you marry me, Miss Leslie? |
| Miss Leslie | No, Mr. Maxwell. |
| Maxwell | *(Disappointed)* Ah! |
| Miss Leslie | I can't marry you. |
| Maxwell | I suppose you can't. I'm sorry. I'm sorry, Miss Leslie. *(He is back to his business manners again.)* Take this letter, please. |
| Miss Leslie | You've been much too busy. |
| Maxwell | Mr. John Smith…What did you say? |
| Miss Leslie | I said you've been much too busy, Harvey. |
| Maxwell | *(A little taken back by Miss Leslie's familiarity)* Miss Leslie, a letter to Mr. John Smith, please. |

| | |
|---|---|
| *Miss Leslie* | Your work just drives everything else you should be thinking of clear out of your mind. |
| *Maxwell* | *(Becoming a little impatient)* Miss Leslie... |
| *Miss Leslie* | Do you know why I can't marry you, Harvey? |
| *Maxwell* | *(Studies Miss Leslie for a moment; then most seriously)* I don't know why not, Miss Leslie. |
| *Miss Leslie* | Because last night, at exactly eight o'clock, in the Little Church Around the Corner, you put this ring on this finger, Harvey Maxwell, and we were married. |

# THE LAST LEAF

## from the story by O. Henry

*This is the story of
a young girl who
feels she must die
when the last leaf
falls from the vine
that grows on the wall
across from her window.*
*As the story begins, there are only twelve leaves on the vine.
It is late in the month of November, and the strong north winds
have come early. How long can those leaves stay on the vine?*

| | |
|---|---|
| THE CAST | *Announcer*<br>*Johnsy* (Her real name is Joanna, and she is a very sick young girl)<br>*Sue* (Johnsy's roommate, an artist, like Johnsy)<br>*The Doctor*<br>*Behrman* (An old artist, a friend of the girls) |
| THE SET | Sue and Johnsy's one-room apartment. There are two small beds, table, chairs, easel, and paints. Through the window can be seen the wall with the vine. |

THE LAST LEAF is an adaptation by Henry Gilfond of
the short story of the same title by O. Henry (William Sydney Porter).
This adaptation © 1966 by Henry Gilfond

| Announcer | Sue and Joanna are young artists. They live in a one-room apartment in an old house. Joanna, who is called Johnsy by her friends, has always wanted to go to Italy to paint the beautiful Bay of Naples, but she is very sick. As the play opens, she is lying in bed and the doctor is examining her. |
|---|---|
| Doctor | *(Holding Johnsy's hand)* You can't let this illness keep you down, Johnsy. You've got to fight to get well and out of bed. |
| Sue | She won't eat anything, Doctor. I've made her soup, and even cooked a chicken. Won't you tell her to eat, Doctor? |
| Doctor | You need to eat, Johnsy. You need strength to battle this sickness of yours. Soup is good for you. So is chicken. You'll have to eat, if you want to get out of bed. |
| Sue | That's what I keep telling her, Doctor. She won't listen to me. Maybe she'll listen to you. |
| Doctor | You had better listen to Sue, Johnsy. She is your nurse, and she is a good nurse. A good friend, too, I think. *(Putting his instruments back into his bag)* I'll see you in the morning. *(Pause)* I'm trying to help you, Johnsy. Sue is trying to help you. You have to try, too. |
| Sue | Thank you, Doctor. |
| Doctor | *(As they walk to the door)* She's a very sick girl. |

| Sue | Is she going to die? |
|---|---|
| Doctor | I can't say. That's up to her. |
| Sue | What does that mean, Doctor? |
| Doctor | Well, the truth is that I don't give her much chance. |
| Sue | Oh! *(Pause)* Is there anything, anything I can do? Isn't there something you can do, Doctor? |
| Doctor | I'm afraid not. It seems to me that she wants to die. She doesn't want to live anymore. I should say that she has one chance in ten of coming through this illness. When a person finds he has nothing to live for, he usually goes. |
| Sue | But Johnsy has so much to live for! She's young. She wants to paint the Bay of Naples. |
| Doctor | The Bay of Naples? That's a long way from here. If there were something else, something right here, next door, across the street, she would have a real chance. If there were a young man . . . |
| Sue | There's no young man. The only thing she wanted badly was to paint the Bay of Naples. |
| Doctor | It isn't enough. Too far away. Sorry. I'm doing my best, Sue. Maybe you can get her to think about a new winter coat, a hat. That would help. She has to have something, anything, to keep her alive. |
| Sue | I wish I knew. I'll try, Doctor. Thank you. |

| | |
|---|---|
| Doctor | Don't thank me. I haven't done anything. Try to get her to eat something. I'll see you in the morning. Good night. |
| Sue | Good night. |
| | *(The doctor leaves. Sue looks at Johnsy for a minute. She picks up her drawing board, tries to look cheerful, sits down beside Johnsy, and begins to draw.)* |
| Sue | I said I'd have this drawing finished for the office by morning. |
| Johnsy | *(Opens her eyes, looks towards the window.)* Twelve. |
| Sue | Are you feeling better, Johnsy? |
| Johnsy | *(After a moment)* Eleven. |
| Sue | The doctor said you'd be up and painting in no time. |
| Johnsy | Ten. Nine. Eight. |
| Sue | *(Worried)* What are you saying. Johnsy? |
| Johnsy | Seven. |
| Sue | What are you counting, Johnsy? What is it? |
| Johnsy | They are falling faster now. There were almost a hundred three days ago. |

| | |
|---|---|
| Sue | Please, Johnsy! I don't understand you at all. Are you all right? |
| Johnsy | It made my head ache to count them. There were so many. Now it is easier. There goes another. There are only six now. |
| Sue | Six what, Johnsy? Won't you please tell me? |
| Johnsy | Six leaves on the ivy vine, the ivy vine growing on the wall. Can't you see them? Through this window? |
| Sue | (Looks) Of course I can see them. But why are you counting them? |
| Johnsy | When the last leaf falls off the vine, I must go, too. |
| Sue | Nonsense, Johnsy! Nonsense! What have old ivy leaves got to do with your getting well? You're being silly, Johnsy. |
| Johnsy | I'm not being silly. I've known it for days. |
| Sue | You're trying to frighten me. You're playing a game. |
| Johnsy | It's not a game, Sue. |
| Sue | But the doctor said it was ten to one you'd be all well fast. Those are better odds than you get crossing a street in New York. |
| Johnsy | Five. |

| Sue | *(Getting up quickly)* That's enough counting, Johnsy. Let me get you some soup. You need to eat to get well. |
|---|---|
| Johnsy | I don't want any soup. There goes another. There are just four now. I want to see the last one fall before it gets dark. Then I'll go, too. |
| Sue | *(Bending over Johnsy, fixing her covers)* Johnsy! Please close your eyes. Don't look out of the window. I have to finish this drawing by morning and I need the light. If I didn't need the light, I'd pull the shade. |
| Johnsy | Then tell me when you're finished. I want to see the last leaf fall. I'm tired of waiting. I'm tired of thinking. I want to go sailing down, down, down, like one of the poor, tired leaves. |
| Sue | Shut your eyes, Johnsy. Try to get a little sleep. |
| | *(A faint knock at the door. Sue answers it quickly and old Behrman enters.)* |
| Sue | Shhh! I think she's sleeping. |
| Behrman | How is she? |
| Sue | Very sick. |
| Behrman | What did the doctor say? |
| Sue | It's bad. It's very bad. *(She begins to cry.)* |

| | |
|---|---|
| *Behrman* | Ah, doctors! She'll get well. |
| *Sue* | *(Shaking her head)* She doesn't want to get well. She says she is going to die when the last leaf falls off the ivy vine. |
| *Behrman* | What leaf? What vine? |
| *Sue* | *(Pointing)* The vine on the backyard wall. |
| *Behrman* | What kind of foolish talk is that? |
| *Sue* | I don't know. She keeps looking at the wall and counting the leaves. When the last leaf falls, she will die. |
| *Behrman* | Foolish! Foolish! I have never heard such talk, so long as I am an artist. |
| *Sue* | Shhh! You'll wake her. |
| *Behrman* | With all the rain and the wind! How long can a leaf stay up there on the wall? |
| *Sue* | *(Crying again)* I don't know. |
| *Behrman* | Sh! Now you'll wake her up with your crying. There is nothing to cry about. *(He walks to the window, lowers the shade.)* Keep the shade down and dry your eyes. I think that maybe that last leaf will never fall from the wall. |
| *Announcer* | That was the end of our first act. The second act opens in the same room, one week later, early in the morning. The window shade is down. Sue is drawing. Johnsy is just waking. |

**112**  *The Last Leaf*

| | |
|---|---|
| *Johnsy* | *(Her voice much stronger than in Act 1)* Sue! |
| *Sue* | Yes, Johnsy? |
| *Johnsy* | The window shade. Please pull it up. |
| *Sue* | *(Going to the window)* Sure. You're still waiting for that last leaf to fall. |
| *Johnsy* | It must have fallen during the night. |
| *Sue* | *(Lifting the shade)* But it didn't. |
| *Johnsy* | It's still there! Seven days now. How can it stay there with all the wind and the rain? A little leaf on an old vine? I just don't know how it does it! |
| *Sue* | It's there, isn't it? |
| *Johnsy* | It's there, all right. |
| *Sue* | And you're getting better every day. |
| *Johnsy* | I think I'm getting better. |
| *Sue* | That's what the doctor says. |
| *Johnsy* | He can't understand that leaf, either. Why doesn't Behrman come to see me any more? He must be too busy painting his masterpiece. He's always working on his masterpiece, the poor old man. Ask him in to breakfast, Sue. |
| *Sue* | Not this morning, Johnsy. |

| | |
|---|---|
| Johnsy | Why not? I'm hungry and I want Behrman to see me eat a big breakfast again. Maybe it'll inspire him. Ask him in. |
| Sue | I can't. |
| Johnsy | Why not? |
| Sue | He's in the hospital. |
| Johnsy | Oh, I'm sorry. I didn't know he was sick. |
| Sue | He's very sick. |
| Johnsy | You should have told me. |
| Sue | There are some things you can't tell a girl who thinks she is going to die with the last leaf on an ivy vine. |
| Johnsy | It didn't die. It didn't want me to die. |
| Sue | I didn't want you to die. Behrman didn't want you to die. |
| | *(Knock at the door)* |
| Johnsy | Maybe it's Behrman. |
| Sue | *(Going to the door)* I wish it were. *(Opens the door)* Come in, Doctor, Good morning. |
| Doctor | Good morning. Well! Good morning, Johnsy. You're looking really bright this morning. |

| | |
|---|---|
| *Johnsy* | I do feel almost all well again, Doctor. |
| *Doctor* | Good. I think you are well again. It was that last leaf. |
| *Johnsy* | It's still there. |
| *Doctor* | It'll be there for a long time. |
| *Johnsy* | Nature is wonderful. |
| *Doctor* | Nature? Did you look at that leaf closely, Johnsy? |
| *Johnsy* | I was waiting for it to fall. |
| *Sue* | *(Interrupting)* How is Behrman, Doctor? |
| *Doctor* | Didn't I tell you? He died last night. |
| *Johnsy* | How terrible! |
| *Doctor* | He was an old man. All that cold rain and the wind were too much for him. It was a brave thing he did. He must have loved you like a father. |
| *Johnsy* | But he was never out in the wind and the rain, Doctor. I don't understand. All he did was to paint pictures inside his little studio. |
| *Doctor* | You want to paint the Bay of Naples, don't you? |
| *Sue* | I told the doctor. |
| *Johnsy* | I think it will be my greatest picture. |
| *Doctor* | Behrman painted his greatest picture just about a week ago, in the wind and the rain. |

| | |
|---|---|
| *Johnsy* | What did he paint? |
| *Doctor* | Leaves flutter in the wind, Johnsy. |
| *Johnsy* | *(Beginning to understand)* Oh! Of course . . . |
| *Doctor* | Have you ever seen that last leaf of yours move? |
| *Johnsy* | Never. |
| *Doctor* | It couldn't. The first night that Sue pulled down the shade, Behrman got himself a ladder and some green paint. He went out into the rain and the wind. He climbed the ladder, and he painted that last leaf on the wall. There were no leaves at all left on the vine when Behrman climbed the ladder. That leaf you've been looking at is Behrman's. That last leaf is Behrman's greatest picture. It's his masterpiece. |

# SHIPWRECK

## from the story by
## Ambrose Bierce

*This story takes place aboard a ship. Or is it two ships? You will have to decide the answer to this question after you have read the story. You will have to decide the answer to several questions. Did William Jarrett sail from Liverpool on the English ship* Morrow? *What happened to Janette Harford? There is an even larger question which the story asks: "Is what a man imagines to be true more true, more real, than what he does?" The full title of the story is "A Psychological Shipwreck." It was written by Ambrose Bierce, who was always concerned with that larger question.*

THE CAST    Announcer           Second Seaman
            William Jarrett      Third Seaman
            Janette Harford      Fourth Seaman
            Hannah               Gordon Doyle
            First Seaman         Steward

THE SETS    A deck on the *Morrow*
            A cabin on the *City of Prague*

SHIPWRECK is an adaptation by Henry Gilfond of
Ambrose Bierce's "A Psychological Shipwreck."

This adaptation © 1966 by Henry Gilfond

| | |
|---|---|
| Announcer | The year is 1874. We are on board the English ship, *Morrow*. At least, we think we are on board the *Morrow*. Janette Harford and William Jarrett are sitting on the deck. Janette has a book in her hands. She is talking to her servant, a woman some years older than Janette. |
| Janette | *(To her servant)* Thank you for bringing the book, Hannah. |
| Hannah | You're welcome, Ma'am. Is there anything else I can do for you? |
| Janette | No, thank you. Oh yes! What is today's date, Hannah? |
| Hannah | Let me think. |
| William Jarrett | July 3rd. |
| Janette | We've been sailing for eighteen days, then. |
| Jarrett | That's right. We left Liverpool the 15th of June. |
| Janette | *(To Hannah)* You may go now if you wish, Hannah. *(Hannah exits.)* |
| Jarrett | Hannah has been with you for a long time, hasn't she? |
| Janette | No. Not very long. She came to my family only a little while ago. She was with a family from South Carolina before she came to us. |
| Jarrett | South Carolina? |

| Janette | Yes. There were just a husband and wife, and they both died quite suddenly while they were visiting my family. |
| Jarrett | Strange. I have family, or had family, in South Carolina. I know some Jarretts settled in South Carolina. But I don't know just where, or what they do. I've had no contact with them at all. |
| Janette | Jarrett! The people who left Hannah with us were named Jarrett. I don't know why I hadn't thought of it before! |
| Jarrett | They might have been my relatives. |
| Janette | They might have been. Jarrett is not a common name. And his first name was William! That's your name! William Jarrett! |
| Jarrett | So it is. But I'm alive. |
| Janette | So you are. So you are. *(She looks out to the sea.)* |
| Jarrett | *(After a moment)* Is there something out there? |
| Janette | There's nothing there but sky and water. |
| Jarrett | I'd swear you were miles and miles away, Miss Harford, searching for something, or maybe searching for someone. |
| Janette | I wasn't searching. I wasn't looking for anything, or anyone. Your imagination is running away with you, Mr. Jarrett. |
| Jarrett | Perhaps. Perhaps you'll tell me some other time. |

| | |
|---|---|
| Janette | *(Opening her book)* There's absolutely nothing to tell. |
| Jarrett | That's a curious book you're reading. *Denneker's Meditations.* Denneker's thoughts. You have an interesting passage right there *(Pointing to a page in the book).* Would you mind reading it to me? |
| Janette | Not at all. *(She reads)* "Some men and women have the power to leave their own bodies, and their spirits may wander about, meeting the spirits of others, spirits they choose to meet, while their bodies do the ordinary things that bodies do, unaware of the fact that their spirits have left them." |
| Jarrett | That's quite a statement. |
| Janette | In other words, my spirit may be far away from here, from this ship, and this deck, while my body stays here and talks to you. |
| Jarrett | Or we both may be spirits, meeting on this ship, and our bodies somewhere else. |
| Janette | That's true. *(She suddenly stands up.)* I'm cold! |
| Jarrett | You must have a chill. It's still quite warm. |
| First Seaman | *(Enters and looks at Janette)* Do you need any help, miss? |
| Jarrett | I'll take care of her, thank you. It's just a chill. |
| First Seaman | *(Looks up at the sky)* It looks as if the weather is changing. |

**124** *Shipwreck*

| | |
|---|---|
| Second Seaman | (Entering) Get to the masts! We're going to have a blow! |
| Third Seaman | (Entering) Storm coming up! |
| Fourth Seaman | (Entering) Better get down below! This is going to blow this old ship apart! |
| Jarrett | (To Janette) Hold my hand! (Both Janette and Jarrett sway, as the ship is hit by the sudden storm.) My hand! |
| Janette | (As if she were far away) Where? Where? |
| Jarrett | Here! Hold my hand! The ship's going down! For God's sake, take my hand! |
| Announcer | She never took his hand. Jarrett reached for her, but the more he reached, the further she was. |
| Jarrett | Miss Harford! Janette! |
| Announcer | He lost her in the wind and the rain, and the sudden darkness that covered the skies. The noise of the waves was stronger than his voice. |
| Jarrett | Janette! Where are you?! Janette! |
| Announcer | It was no use. Suddenly, Jarrett blacked out. The last thing that he remembered was that he had tied himself to a floating mast. How long could he live in the violent sea? This is the first part of the story. Let us move now to the second part. Gordon Doyle is sitting on a couch in a ship's cabin. Lying on the cot is William Jarrett, fast asleep. |

| | |
|---|---|
| Steward | *(Entering)* Did you call, sir? |
| Doyle | Some fresh water, if we can have it. |
| Steward | Right away, sir! *(He exits.)* |
| Jarrett | *(Wakes. Looks at Doyle, puzzled.)* Doyle! |
| Doyle | *(Rises. Gets himself a book. Returns to his chair.)* Well? |
| Jarrett | Did they save her? Janette Harford? |
| Doyle | Janette Harford? |
| Jarrett | Ah. You don't want to say. The storm came up so suddenly, there wasn't a chance. All right, Doyle. I understand well enough. You'll tell me after a while. |
| Doyle | *(Looks at Jarrett. Doyle is puzzled.)* Yes. Yes, I'll tell you everything in a little while. |
| Jarrett | Thank you. *(He lies back on his cot, then suddenly rises.)* What ship is this? What is the name of this ship we're on? |
| Doyle | It's called the *City of Prague*. Left Liverpool three weeks ago, and we're sailing with a broken shaft. |
| Jarrett | *City of Prague*. Of course. I saw you off at the pier. You asked me to join you. Of course. |
| Doyle | Now look here, Jarrett, I don't know what's got into you, but there are just two passengers on this ship. Mr. Gordon Doyle and a lunatic by the name of William Jarrett. |

| Jarrett | I've been a passenger on this boat for three weeks!? |
|---|---|
| Doyle | Come on now, Jarrett. Enough of this game. It's just about three weeks. Today's the third of July. |
| Jarrett | *(Remembering the date: the third of July)* Have I been ill? |
| Doyle | Ill? You've been as healthy as a dray-horse, and at the table for your meals the minute they've called you. |
| Jarrett | My God, Doyle! There's a mystery here. |
| Doyle | Sure there is a mystery. Now you tell me all about it. |
| Jarrett | Be serious, Doyle, I beg you. Didn't the steamship *Morrow* sink in the storm? And wasn't I rescued from its wreck? |
| Doyle | *(Changing his tone sharply)* The steamship *Morrow?* |
| Jarrett | Wasn't I saved from its wreck? |
| Doyle | What do you know about Janette Harford? |
| Jarrett | We were...You tell me what *you* know about her first. |
| Doyle | *(After a moment)* Why shouldn't I? I'm engaged to marry Janette Harford. I met her a year ago in London. She comes from one of the richest families in England. We eloped...or, I should say, we are eloping. She didn't want to take this |

**128** *Shipwreck*

boat, *City of Prague*. She thought it would be better if we took different boats. People see and people talk. We didn't want anything to interfere with this marriage. So she took the *Morrow*. She went with an old family servant. Hannah, I think they call her. What worries me now is the broken shaft on this ship of ours. The *Morrow* will get to New York before us, and poor Janette won't know where to go.

Jarrett    You're very much in love.

Doyle    Of course. *(Pause)* By the way, she is not really a Harford. Her mother was thrown from a horse and killed. Her father was so maddened by his wife's death that he killed himself. The Harfords adopted her, though she doesn't know it.

Jarrett    *(To himself)* Janette Harford. *(He glances at the book in Doyle's hands.)* What are you reading, Doyle?

Doyle    Some odd book Janette gave me. *Denneker's Meditations*. She had two copies. She gave me one. Do you want to see it? *(He tosses the book to Jarrett)*

Jarrett    *(Catches the book. It has opened to a particular page. Jarrett reads it aloud.)* "Some men and women have the power to leave their own bodies, and their spirits may wander about, meeting the spirits of others, spirits they choose to meet, while their bodies do the ordinary things that bodies do, unaware of the fact that their spirits have left them."

| Doyle | I told you it was an odd book. Now you tell me what you know about Janette Harford, and how you happen to know the name of the boat she sailed on. |
|---|---|
| Jarrett | You talked about her in your sleep. |
| Doyle | *(Laughing)* I did? |
| Jarrett | You did. |
| | *(Steward knocks at the door)* |
| Jarrett | Who's that? |
| Doyle | The steward with some fresh water. Come in! |
| Announcer | The steamship *City of Prague* came into the port of New York one week later. But the *Morrow* was never heard from. |

# THE CELEBRATED JUMPING FROG OF CALAVERAS COUNTY

## from the story by Mark Twain

*Mark Twain could tell a funny story, and this story is one of his best. The hero of this tale might be easy-going Smiley, who would bet on anything from a cat fight to a dog race. Or the hero might be Smiley's famous frog. Or it might be the stranger who, during an unusually quiet moment of the great 1849 California Gold Rush, walked into Angel's Camp. This is not a story about gold, although Smiley was always interested in the precious metal, especially when it belonged to somebody else. It is a simple story about two men, a frog, and a bet Angel's Camp never forgot.*

THE CAST      *Smiley* (A lazy, easy-going gold miner)
                       *Stranger* (A man who needs to see something to believe it)
                       *Daniel Webster* (Smiley's frog)
                       *Three Men of Angel's Camp*

THE SET       Angel's Camp

THE CELEBRATED JUMPING FROG OF CALAVERAS COUNTY is an adaptation by Henry Gilfond of the short story of the same title by Mark Twain (Samuel L. Clemens).

This adaptation © 1966 by Henry Gilfond

**131**

*Stranger*

*Smiley*

*Stranger*

*Smiley*

*Stranger*

*Smiley*

*Stranger*

*Smiley*

*Stranger*

*Smiley*

*Stranger*

*Smiley*

*Stranger*

*Smiley*

*Stranger*

*Smiley*

*Stranger*


*Smiley*

*Stranger*


*Smiley*

*(Smiley is looking at a box, and the Stranger is looking at both Smiley and his box.)*

What's that you've got in that box, Smiley?

What do you think?

I wouldn't know.

*(Cunningly)* It might be a parrot.

It might be.

It might be, but it isn't.

It isn't a very big box.

No, but it's big enough for a canary. It might be a canary.

It might be.

It might, but it isn't.

It might be a horse.

You never saw a horse that would fit into this box.

No, but I might.

You might not.

I guess you're right. I might not.

It's a frog!

*(Takes box from Smiley, looks into it)* Hmmm. So it is. It's a frog. What do you want with a frog in a box? It doesn't make any sense, keeping a frog in a box.

Do you know any better place to keep him?

I don't know much about keeping frogs, but I wouldn't keep him in a box.

You would, if his name was Daniel Webster. Daniel Webster's quite a frog.

*Stranger*

*Smiley*

*Stranger*

*Smiley*

*Stranger*

*Smiley*

*Stranger*

*Smiley*

*Stranger*

*Smiley*

*Stranger*

*Smiley*

*Stranger*

*Smiley*

*Stranger*

*Smiley*

*Stranger*

*Stranger*

Yes? He looks like any other frog to me.

Maybe he does look like any other frog to you. You're a stranger around this camp, aren't you?

I've been around, I've seen frogs before.

You've never seen anyone like Daniel Webster before.

I've never heard of a frog called Daniel Webster before.

That's because you've never met up with a frog like Daniel Webster.

Maybe.

Daniel Webster is a special kind of frog. He's a champion frog.

Champion frog? Champion what?

I was thinking of telling you.

Go ahead. Tell me.

I was just *thinking* of telling you.

Oh! You're making up your mind?

I've made up my mind.

Are you going to tell me? Are you going to tell me what's special about Daniel Webster? Are you going to tell me what makes him a champion?

If you give me a chance.

I'm listening.

*(Smiley looks at the Stranger, not sure now that he wants to tell him.)*

Come on, Smiley. What's special about this Daniel Webster you got in your box?

*Smiley*

*Stranger*
*Smiley*
*Stranger*
*Smiley*
*Stranger*

*Smiley*

*Smiley*
*Stranger*

*Smiley*
*Stranger*
*Smiley*
*Stranger*
*Smiley*

Best jumping frog in Angel's Camp. That's what's special about Daniel Webster. Best jumping frog in Angel's Camp. Best jumping frog in all of Calaveras County, if you want to know. The champion jumping frog in Calaveras County. That's what's special about Daniel Webster. And that's why I keep him in this box.

Maybe you're right.

You can bet your last dollar I'm right.

And maybe you're wrong.

Wrong?

He still looks like any other frog to me. Daniel Webster and any other frog I've seen, they all look alike to me. They're just frogs.

Well, stranger, maybe you know frogs and maybe you don't. I've got my way of thinking about frogs and maybe you've got your way of thinking about frogs. I'll tell you what. I'm willing to risk forty dollars on Daniel Webster. I'm willing to bet you forty dollars you can't find a frog in all of Calaveras County can jump better than he can.

*(Stranger studies Daniel Webster for a moment.)*

Well?

I'm just a stranger in this camp, Smiley, but if I had a frog, I'd bet you the forty dollars.

You would?

That's what I said.

If you had a frog, you'd bet me? I'll get you a frog.

What kind of frog?

A good jumping frog. Just hold onto my box, and I'll have you a frog in a minute.

*Stranger*

*Smiley*

*Stranger*


*1st Camper*

*Stranger*

*2nd Camper*

*Stranger*

*3rd Camper*

*Stranger*


*1st Camper*

*Stranger*

*2nd Camper*

*Stranger*

*3rd Camper*

*Stranger*


*1st Camper*


*Stranger*


*Smiley*

You got Daniel Webster in the box?

See that he doesn't follow me. I'll be back. *(He exits.)*

*(Shouting after Smiley)* I'll take care of him, Smiley. (He begins to take something from his pocket, and feeds it to Daniel Webster.

(Three campers enter.)

Howdy. That's Smiley's frog, isn't it?

It's Daniel Webster, all right.

Where's Smiley?

He went to find another frog.

He didn't sell you Daniel, did he?

No. He's looking for another frog to jump against this Webster frog.

He didn't ask you to feed Daniel?

No, but he looks hungry.

Those aren't flies you're feeding him.

No, but it isn't poison either.

That's one way to win a bet.

I never liked to lose one. I don't know anybody who does. But I'm not aiming to poison Daniel Webster.

That would make Smiley awfully mad. You sure are feeding him enough. He looks stuffed.

He was mighty hungry.


*(Entering with another frog)* Here I am, and here's your frog, stranger. You still want to bet, don't you?

Stranger

Smiley


Stranger
Smiley
2nd Camper
Smiley
2nd Camper
Smiley

Stranger
Smiley
2nd Camper


Smiley
Stranger
Smiley
1st Camper
2nd Camper
Smiley

Stranger

**140** *The Celebrated Jumping Frog*

*(Takes his frog, looks at it.) (Taking the money from his pocket)* Forty dollars.

*(Getting his own money from his pockets)* Put it right down on the table. Here's mine. Count it, fellows. Easy money! *(To Stranger)* Here! Set your frog next to Daniel. Get their paws even.

They're even.

Now you fellows watch and see that this bet is fair and square.

We're watching.

All right. *(To 2nd Camper)* You say, "One, two, three, go!"

I'll start them.

*(To Stranger)* When he says go, we touch the frogs from behind. The one who jumps farthest wins.

That's the general idea.

*(To 2nd camper)* Start counting!

All right. One! Two! Three! Go!

*(Smiley and the Stranger touch their frogs. The Stranger's frog leaps, but Daniel Webster doesn't move at all.)*

*(Pushing his frog from behind)* Go! Go! Go, Daniel! Go!

What's the matter with your frog, Smiley?

I don't know. He never acted this way before. Go, Daniel! Go!

He must be tired.

Maybe he's just worn out.

*(Pleading)* Go, Daniel! Something is wrong. What's the matter, Daniel?

I guess I win the bet.

*Smiley*

*Stranger*


*Campers*

*Smiley*

*1st Camper*

*Smiley*


*2nd Camper*

*Smiley*

*3rd Camper*

*1st Camper*

*Smiley*

*2nd Camper*

*Smiley*


*1st Camper*

*2nd Camper*

*Smiley*

*3rd Camper*

*Announcer*

I can't understand. Daniel never let me down before.

(Taking the money from the table) I'll be collecting the money now. I never did think your frog was better than any other frog. I guess he isn't. So long, Smiley. Thanks for the forty dollars. So long, fellows. (He leaves.)

(As the Stranger leaves) So long, stranger.

What happened to you, Daniel?

Maybe he's sick.

(Picking up his frog) He's never been sick before. Say! He's heavy! He must weigh about five pounds.

The stranger was feeding him.

He was? (Buckshot falls out of the frog's mouth) What's this?

Lead!

That's what the stranger was feeding him. Buckshot!

I've been fooled!

You can say that again, Smiley!

Where is he? He can't do this to me! I'll get that thief! My forty dollars!

He must be forty miles out of camp by now.

More like a hundred.

I'll get him! Filling my Daniel Webster with lead!

Want to bet on it, Smiley?

Smiley didn't make any more bets that afternoon. And he never caught up with the stranger, nor with the forty dollars he had bet on Daniel Webster.

# THE UPHEAVAL

## from the story by
## Anton Chekhov

*A valuable brooch has been stolen. The lady of the house suspects everyone. The servants have been questioned and Masha, the young governess, is not above suspicion. Who stole the brooch? The answer to this question will come as a surprise. More important in the story is the manner in which Masha reacts to her mistress's suspicion.*

| | |
|---|---|
| THE CAST | *Announcer* |
| | *Madame Kushkin* |
| | *Masha* |
| | *Liza* |
| | *Olga* (A servant) |
| | *Nicholas Kushkin* |
| | |
| THE SET | Masha's room in the Kushkin house |

THE UPHEAVAL is an adaptation by Henry Gilfond of the short story of the same title by Anton Chekhov.

This adaptation © 1966 by Henry Gilfond

**146** *The Upheaval*

| | |
|---|---|
| Announcer | The story opens with Madame Kushkin making a thorough search of Masha's room. She tries to put things back as they were, but she is in a hurry and very tense. A drawer in a chest has been closed, but not too tightly. A basket has been emptied and its contents returned, but it is obvious that the basket has been searched. She has just upset a work basket — balls of wool, scraps of material, papers — when Masha enters. For a brief moment, they look at each other. |
| Madame Kushkin | I'm sorry. I upset the basket quite by accident. My sleeve got caught on it. |
| Masha | But, Madame Kushkin? |
| Madame Kushkin | I'm sorry. I said I'm sorry! *(She walks out in a great hurry.)* |
| Masha | *(To herself, as she examines the upheaval and begins to put things together again)* What was she doing in my room? *(There is a knock at the door.)* Come in. |
| Liza | It's terrible, isn't it? |
| Masha | I don't know. Everyone seemed upset when I came in. |
| Liza | Everyone *is* upset. |
| Masha | Look at this room, will you? What have they been doing in my room, Liza? |
| Liza | Madame has lost a brooch. |
| Masha | I'm sorry to hear it, but she couldn't have lost it here. She has never been in this room all the time I've lived here. |

*The Upheaval*   **147**

| | |
|---|---|
| *Liza* | It's a very valuable brooch. It cost two thousand rubles. |
| *Masha* | That's a lot of money, but why my room? Look at the mess they've made! |
| *Liza* | They've searched everyone. They've searched all my things, too. They stripped us naked, every one of us, and searched us. |
| *Masha* | How dreadful! |
| *Liza* | The Lord knows that I never went anywhere near her dressing table. That's where she keeps her box of jewelry. And I never touched her brooch. I'll tell them so at the police station, if they ask me. |
| *Masha* | Yes, of course. But why my room? |
| *Liza* | I've just told you. Madame's brooch has been stolen. She is turning the house upside down. She won't trust anybody. She even searched Michael, the porter, and he's been with the family for so many years. |
| *Masha* | Disgraceful! |
| *Liza* | And the Master just looks on. He cackles like a hen. He doesn't like the whole thing one bit! |
| *Masha* | I can't blame him. |
| *Liza* | Neither do I. Madame is such a bad-tempered shrew. But you don't have to worry. They didn't find anything here. |
| *Masha* | But it's low! It's insulting! It's vile! How dared she suspect me of taking her brooch? What right did she have to upset everything in my room? |

| | |
|---|---|
| Liza | That's what Master Nicholas said. He shouted it. "Vile! Stupid! Barbarous!" he shouted. But Madam didn't pay any attention to him. She never does. |
| Masha | They had no right to do it! |
| Liza | You are living with strangers, Masha. You're a young lady, and you've been educated, but... you're not living home. You're a servant here, too, Masha, for all your being a young lady and educated. |
| Masha | *(Beginning to cry)* I won't be dragged off by the police. My father is a school teacher. I come from a good family. They're not going to search me like a criminal. They're not going to strip me of my clothes and search me and send me to some dark cell in a prison, full of mice and lice. |
| Liza | Masha! Masha! They didn't find anything in your room! |
| Masha | I'm not a thief! I'll tell them all. I'll tell all the police! I'll go to all the courts! I'll tell all the lawyers! I'll swear to it! |
| Olga | *(Knocks at the door, opens it)* Dinner is being served. |
| Masha | I won't eat at their table! |
| Liza | Then you'll be hungry. |
| Masha | I'd rather be hungry than eat at their table. |
| Liza | That's silly. *(She begins to help Masha get ready for dinner.)* Here. Dry your eyes. Comb your hair. Fix your dress. It's a pretty dress. |

**150** *The Upheaval*

| | |
|---|---|
| Masha | *(Allowing Liza to help her)* I really shouldn't eat at their table. |
| Liza | But you've done nothing wrong. It's Madame who has been vile. She'll eat her dinner, and with a good appetite. Why should you go hungry? |
| Announcer | Masha went in to dinner, but she didn't stay long. She didn't like the conversation at the table, nor way everyone seemed to look at her. With a quick, "Excuse me. I've a headache," she left the table and returned to her own room, where she immediately began to pack her things into her two suitcases. Master Nicholas was not far behind her. |
| Nicholas | *(Knocking at the door)* May I come in? *(He knocks more sharply.)* Masha! May I come in? |
| Masha | Come in. |
| Nicholas | *(Enters. He looks at Masha's suitcases.)* You're straightening out your things? You're packing? But you mustn't go! |
| Masha | I wish I had a horse and carriage. I wish I had inherited a fortune. I could leave in style, then. |
| Nicholas | I don't blame you, Masha, but you're not doing the right thing. |
| Masha | After my room has been searched? After I've been treated like a common thief? |
| Nicholas | So they searched you? They found nothing here. Why do you have to make such a fuss over it? |
| Masha | You don't understand, do you? |

| Nicholas | What shall I do? You know how nervous my wife is, how stubborn. Don't judge her too harshly. Look at the way she speaks to me at the dinner table. I asked the cook to prepare some fish for dinner, but my wife doesn't like fish. Do I get fish for dinner? No! Do I condemn her for it? No! Besides, she is worried about the brooch. "It cost two thousand," she cries, and there are tears in her eyes. Please, Masha. |
|---|---|
| Masha | She searched my room. That is enough. That is too much for me. You make allowances for your wife. I can't. |
| Nicholas | I'll apologize. I'm sorry. I ask your pardon. |
| Masha | *(Who continues packing throughout the scene)* I did not ask for your apologies. |
| Nicholas | I apologize for my wife. As I am a gentleman, she behaved without any tact. |
| Masha | Please! |
| Nicholas | Please! Please, please! You want this thing to eat at my heart! You want my conscience to plague me! |
| Masha | I'm sorry. I can't do anything else. Maybe it is a matter of pride, but I must go away. Please! |
| Nicholas | Your pride! Do you want me to go down on my knees and beg you to stay? |
| Masha | Let me pack. Let me go away. |

| | |
|---|---|
| Nicholas | Ah, Masha! It's all a misunderstanding. Misunderstandings torture me. You have pride. You are packing. You are crying. And you are going away. I have pride, too! And you won't let me keep it! |
| Masha | Pride! She didn't search your room, did she? |
| Nicholas | *(Suddenly very quiet)* No. She didn't search my room. |
| Masha | Then don't talk to me of pride, and let me go about my business. The sooner I leave, the happier for all of us. |
| Nicholas | *(Still quiet)* Masha. Would you have me tell you something I would not tell even at confession? |
| Masha | No. I don't want you to tell me anything. |
| Nicholas | Masha. I'm going to tell you something I won't tell my priest, even on my deathbed. |
| Masha | I'm deaf. I can't hear you. Please! |
| Nicholas | It was I who took my wife's brooch. |
| Masha | *(Looks up, startled)* I don't believe it. You're just trying to keep me here. |
| Nicholas | No, Masha. I stole my wife's brooch. *(Quickly)* Of course, you won't say a word about it? I'm counting on that. You won't even drop the least hint about it, will you? |
| Masha | *(Still not able to believe)* *You* took the brooch? |
| Nicholas | And why shouldn't I? I need the money! |

*The Upheaval* 153

**154**  *The Upheaval*

Masha      (Her mind still on the theft, and not quite able to understand) But why?

Nicholas   She has it all, and she won't give me any of it! It was my father's money! All of it! My father's money bought the house, the furniture! My father's money pays for the servants and the food and everything else!

           (Masha is about to speak, but doesn't. She begins to pack her things again, more quickly than ever.)

Nicholas   (Who has begun to pace the floor, and stops only occasionally to make his argument stronger) And that brooch! It belonged to my mother! It's mine! And she got her hands on it, and wouldn't let go! What should I do? Take her to court? Sue her? I can't do that, can I? Tell me, Masha! Tell me! Can I?

Masha      (She is a little frightened now, as well as angry.) I don't know.

Nicholas   Of course I can't! And I need money. A man needs money. I took the brooch. It's mine, isn't it? (He calms down for a moment, sees Masha has not stopped her packing.) Please, Masha. You see how it is now. Forget she was ever in your room. Stay, Masha.

Masha      (Very unhappily) I can't.

Nicholas   To know all is to forgive all. Forgive, Masha, and stay.

Masha      (After a short pause, and this time most firmly) No! I'll not stay!

| | |
|---|---|
| Nicholas | *(More quietly)* So you won't stay? After all I've told you, you won't stay? |
| Masha | *(Firmly)* No! Now won't you please leave me alone? |
| Nicholas | *(Sighs)* God bless you. I must admit I still admire people who have pride. I admire people who don't forgive too easily. You look so angry, and I could sit here forever and look at your angry face. You won't stay? I understand. That's the way it has to be. It's all right for you. But me? Woe...! I can't take a step out of this house. Even if I did, there'd be one of my wife's rascals to tell me to get off the grass. |
| Madame Kushkin | *(Off stage)* Nicholas! Nicholas! Olga! Go call the master. |
| Nicholas | That sweet voice! *(He laughs bitterly.)* *(To Masha)* You won't stay? You might, you know. I could come and talk with you in the evenings? No? Stay, Masha! Stay! If you go, there won't be a single human being to look at in this awful house! *He exits.)* |
| Masha | *(Stops packing long enough to look at the door Nicholas has closed behind him. She resumes her packing.)* How loathsome! How ugly! |
| Announcer | And in half an hour, Masha was gone. She wouldn't be there when the next piece of jewelry was stolen. |